the survivor songbook 5

D1644829

For information about the above licences contact:
CCL (Europe), P.O. Box 1339, Eastbourne, East Sussex, BN21 1AD
Website: www.ccli.com / e-mail: info@ccli.co.uk / Tel: 01323 417711

ISBN 9781842913970

Compiled by Sally Johnson, Les Moir & Adrian Thompson

CD-Rom compiled by Chris Tice

Music setting and arranging by Paul Hughes & David Ball.

Storylines published by Survivor
Crazy Love published by David C. Cook

Thanks to: Sally Johnson, Mary Prentice, Adrian Thompson, Matt Weeks , Sue Lockhart, EMICMG, Chris
Tice and Paul Johnson.

Cover Design: Dan Armstrong

Printed in the United Kingdom by Yeomans for SURVIVOR, 26-28 Lottbridge Drove, Eastbourne, East
Sussex, BN23 6NT, UK.

Contents

A FRAME SO BEAUTIFULLY FORMED

1.

(All my shame)

Ben and Hannah Dunnett

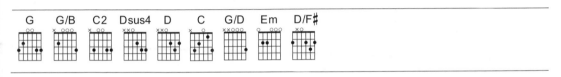

Capo 3

Verse 1:

```
G                      G/B  C2
  A frame so beautifully formed,
G/B                         Dsus4    D
  Brought to life by God's own breath.
G              G/B     C2   C
  Crafted from the planet's dust,
G/D                         G
  God's own image carved in flesh.
                    G/B   C2
But not one righteousness remains,
G/B                         Dsus4   D
  Perfection lost and beauty stained.
G                   G/B   C2  C
  Far from the safety of God's side,
G/D                         G
  Innocence traded for a lie.
```

Chorus:

```
C   D   G
All my shame,
C     D     Em
All I've failed to be,
C/E     D/F#  G
Nailed upon a   cross,
    G/D   D     G
And left at Calvary.
```

Verse 2:

A world of fabulous design
Yet scarred with misery and pain.
But underneath this brokeness,
Our Maker's signature remains.
And only Your redeeming love
Can pay the debt we can't afford.
Salavation worked by Your own hand,
Your broken workmanship restored.

Taken from
THE PEOPLE'S ALBUM, 3,
SURCD5140

ALL OF YOUR QUESTIONS

Come as you are

Tré & Tori Sheppard
& Kathryn Scott

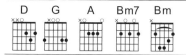

D G A Bm7 Bm

Intro: D G D G

Verse 1:
```
D                          A
All of your questions and all that you hide,
   Bm7                        G
And all that is certain's that you're hollow inside.
     D                        A
When all of your hopes and your plans fall apart,
   Bm7                    G
And none of it even makes sense in your heart.
```

Chorus:
```
D                   A
Come, come as you are
                 Bm            G
With everything broken, all that's not spoken.
D                   A
Come, come as you are
                 Bm              G
Even if it's all over, I've got ev'rything covered: [Last time - end]
                 D   G
Come as you are,
                 D   G
Come as you are.
[2nd time:]
                         D   G
You can come as you are,
                 D   G
Come as you are.
```

Verse 2:
```
All of your heartache and all of your pain,
All of the wounds, the tears and the stains.
Come with your sorrows, your guilt and your shame.
Come when you've got only you left to blame.
```

Mid section:
```
A          Bm   G
There's a place  - here on my shoulder
        A       Bm   G
Where you can rest    'til you're not afraid.
A          Bm   G
Time can wait  - just for a moment
        A    Bm       G
And I will keep you safe.
```

Taken from
AS SURE AS THE STARS
Onehundredhours
SURCD5089

ALL THE HEAVENS PRAISE
(Great and glorious)

Jo Petch

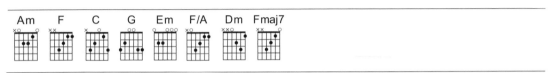

Am   F   C   G   Em   F/A   Dm   Fmaj7

Capo 5

Verse:
```
Am                    F                C            G
  All the heavens praise    Your wonderful ways,    O God.
Am                    F                C            G
  Choirs of angels sing,    sing of all You've done,    O God.
Am                    F              C            G
  Every knee will bow    to worship at Your throne,    O God.
Am                    F              C                         G
  Every heart will cry:    'Holy is Your name,    holy is Your name'.
```

Chorus:
```
F                    C
Great and glorious,
        Em            Am
You reign,    You reign.
        F              C            G
All the heavens and the earth cry out in praise.   [Repeat - but not 1st x]
```

Mid section:
```
          F         G
There's no one higher, no one greater,
    F             G
No one is more powerful.
          F         G                F/A   G
There's no one wiser, no one stronger than You.
          F         G
There's no one higher, no one greater,
    F             G
No one is more powerful.
          Dm            G              F         G
There's no one wiser, no one stronger than You.   Our God.
```

Coda:
```
G                      Fmaj7
  There's no one like You, God. [Repeat x5]
```

ALL WHO ARE THIRSTY

4.

Brenton Brown

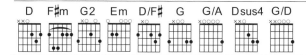

Verse:
        F(D)   Am(F♯m)
All who are thirsty and all who are weak,
     Bb2(G2)   Gm(Em) F/A(D/F♯) Bb(G)
Come to the fountain, dip your heart in the streams of   life.
  Bb/C(G/A)   F(D)   Am(F♯m)
Let the pain and the sorrow be washed away
         Bb2(G2)   Gm(Em) F/A(D/F♯) Bb(G)
In the waves of His mercy as deep cries out   to   deep.
C7sus4(A7sus4)
We sing:

Chorus 1 & 3:
F(D)   Fsus4(Dsus4) Bb/F(G/D) F(D) Bb2(G2)
Come, Lord   Je   -   sus, come.
F(D)   Fsus4(Dsus4) Bb/F(G/D) F(D) Bb2(G2)
Come, Lord   Je   -   sus, come.
F(D)   Fsus4(Dsus4) Bb/F(G/D) F(D) Bb2(G2)
Come, Lord   Je   -   sus, come.
F(D)   Fsus4(Dsus4) Bb/F(G/D) F(D) Bb2(G2)
Come, Lord   Je   -   sus, come.

Chorus 2:
Holy Spirit, come.
Holy Spirit, come.
Holy Spirit, come.
Holy Spirit, come.

Mid section:
         Gm(Em) F/A(D/F♯) Bb(G)
As deep cries out   to   deep.
         Gm(Em) F/A(D/F♯) Bb(G)
As deep cries out   to   deep.
         Gm(Em) F/A(D/F♯) Bb(G)
As deep cries out   to   deep.
C7sus4(A7sus4)
We sing:

Taken from
BECAUSE OF YOUR LOVE
Brenton Brown
SURCD5124

AMAZING GRACE

(Grace flows down)

David Bell, Louie Giglio
& Rod Padgett

5.

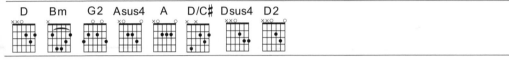

D   Bm   G2   Asus4   A   D/C♯   Dsus4   D2

```
D                 Bm
  Amazing grace
G2                    Asus4   A
  How sweet the sound;
D                 Bm
  Amazing love,
G2                Asus4   A
  Now flowing down
G                 Asus4   A
  From hands and feet
          D     D/C♯     Bm   A
That were nailed to   the tree
G                     Asus4
  As grace flows down
              D   Dsus4
And covers me.


D             G2   Asus4
  It covers me,
A         G   Asus4
  It covers me,
A             G2   Asus4
  It covers me,
A            D2  Bm   G2   Asus4   A   D
  And covers me.
```

Taken from
BEST OF PASSION
(So far)
SURCD5093

AMAGING GRACE

(My chains are gone)

John Newton (1725-1807)/John P Rees (18-28-1900) &
Edwim Othello Excell (1851-1921) / Additional choruses by Chris Tomlin & Louie Giglio

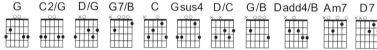

G C2/G D/G G7/B C Gsus4 D/C G/B Dadd4/B Am7 D7

Verse 1:
```
      G               C2/G        G
Amazing grace, how sweet the sound,
                          D/G
That saved a wretch like me.
 G        G7/B   C        G
I once was lost but now I'm found,
              D/G     G [ Gsus4  G]
Was  blind but now I see.   [Not v. 1]
```

Verse 2:
T'was grace that taught my heart to fear,
And grace my fears relieved.
How precious did that grace appear
The hour I first believed.

Chorus:
```
         C   D/C        G/B    Dadd4/B
My chains are gone, I've been set free,
         C   D/C        G/B    Dadd4/B
My God, my Saviour has ransomed me.
       C   D/C      G/B       Dadd4/B
And like a flood His mercy reigns,
          Am7  D7            [1.3. G   D/G   G   D/G]
Unending love,    amazing grace. [2.   G   G/B]
```

Verse 3:
The Lord has promised good to me,
His word, my hope secures.
He will my shield and portion be,
As long as life endures.

Verse 4:
The earth shall soon dissolve like snow,
The sun forbear to shine.
But God who called me here below
```
     G    D/G  G  C/G  G
Will be forever mine.
```

John Newton (1725-1807)/John P Rees (1828-1900)
& Edwin Othello Excell (1851-1921)

Taken from
SEE THE MORNING
Chris Tomlin
SURCD5084

AND THE PROBLEM IS THIS

Surely we can change

7.

David Crowder

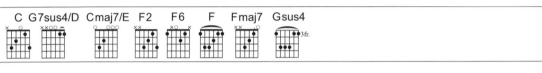

C   G7sus4/D   Cmaj7/E   F2   F6   F   Fmaj7   Gsus4

Capo 3

Verse 1:
```
        Db(C)  Ab7sus4/Eb(G7sus4/D)   Db(C)  Ab7sus4/Eb(G7sus4/D)
And the problem              is this:
        Db(C)  Ab7sus4/Eb(G7sus4/D)   Dbmaj7/F(Cmaj7/E)
We were bought with a kiss,
        Db(C)  Ab7sus4/Eb(G7sus4/D)   Db(C)  Ab7sus4/Eb(G7sus4/D)
But the cheek still          turned
      Db(C)  Ab7sus4/Eb(G7sus4/D)   Dbmaj7/F(Cmaj7/E)
Even when it wasn't hit.
          Gb2(F2)  Gb6(F6)  Gb2(F2)
And I don't know
        Db(C)       Ab7sus4/Eb(G7sus4/D)   Dbmaj7/F(Cmaj7/E)
What to do with a love like          that.
          Gb2(F2)  Gb6(F6)  Gb2(F2)
And I don't know
        Db(C)       Ab7sus4/Eb(G7sus4/D)   Dbmaj7/F(Cmaj7/E)
How to be     a love like             that.
```

Bridge:
```
              Gb(F)    Gbmaj7(Fmaj7)    Gb(F)    Gbmaj7(Fmaj7)
When all the love        in the world
        Db(C)  Ab7sus4/Eb(G7sus4/D)   Dbmaj7/F(Cmaj7/E)     Gb(F)   Gbmaj7(Fmaj7)
Is right here                  among us, and hatred too.
              Db(C)  Ab7sus4/Eb(G7sus4/D)   Dbmaj7/F(Cmaj7/E)
And so we must choose what           our hands will do.
```

Chorus 1:
```
          Gb(F)                Db(C)
Where there is pain, let there be grace.
          Gb(F)                Db(C)
Where there is suffering, bring serenity.
          Gb(F)               Db(C)
For those afraid, help them be brave.
            Gb(F)              Db(C)
Where there is misery, bring expectancy.
      Absus4(Gsus4)     Gb(F)
And surely we can change,
      Absus4(Gsus4) Gb(F)  Gb2(F2)
Surely we can change,      something.
```
```
Db(C)   Ab7sus4/Eb(G7sus4/D)   Dbmaj7/F(Cmaj7/E)
Db(C)   Ab7sus4/Eb(G7sus4/D)   Dbmaj7/F(Cmaj7/E)
```

Chorus 2:
```
Where there is pain, let us bring grace.
Where there is suffering, bring serenity.
For those afraid, let us be brave.
Where there is misery, let us bring relief.
And surely we can change,
   Absus4(Gsus4)      Gb(F)
Surely we can change,
Surely we can change something.
```

Ending:
```
                              Absus4(Gsus4)
And the world's about to change,
                Gb2(F2)       Absus4(Gsus4)
The whole world's about to change, [X3]
                Gb2(F2)               Db(C)
The whole world's about to change.
```

Verse 2:
And the problem it seems is with you and me,
Not the Love who came to repair everything.
And I don't know what to do with a love like that.
And I don't know how to be a love like that.

Taken from
REMEDY
David Crowder Band
SURCD5101

ANOTHER ROUND, ANOTHER DAY

8.

Home

Tré & Tori Sheppard, Mark Prentice,
Paul Baker, Jonny Ravn & Steve Evans

D   G/B   C   C/D   G/D   Am7/D   C/E   D/F#   B♭6

Verse 1:
D   G/B   C
    Another round, another day,
D   G/B   C
    You gotta take each moment, 'cause the time just slips away.
 D   G/B   C
I breathe and close my eyes;
    D   G/B   C
When I'm with you, yeah, I'm glad to be alive.

Chorus 1&2:
D   G/B   C
I, I know you are on my side.
    D   G/B   C
When I'm with you, yeah, it makes me feel alright.
    D   G/B   C
It's something I can't hide.
D   G/B   C
Love can save your life.

Verse 2:
It has occurred to me that I can't always see
Just who I am with all these possibilities.
So I just want to be
The one I am when you are here and close to me.

Mid section:
D   C/D   G/D   Am7/D
I just wanna lay my burdens down.
D   C/E   D/F#   B♭6
Can You help me lay my burdens down?

Chorus 3:

| D | D | G/B | C | D | D | G/B | C |

    D   G/B   C
You make me feel alright
D   G/B   C   D
Love can save your life.

Taken from
AS SURE AS THE STARS
Onehundredhours
SURCD5089

AS WE COME INTO YOUR PRESENCE

Because of Your love

Paul Baloche & Brenton Brown

G/B   C2   Dsus4   G   C   D

Verse:
```
      G/B      C2      Dsus4  G
As we come into Your pre  -  sence,
      G/B      C2    Dsus4  G
We remember every bless - ing
         G/B      C2     Dsus4  G/B      C2
That You've poured out so freely   from above.
      G/B  C2      Dsus4  G
Lifting gratitude and prai - ses
      G/B     C2  Dsus4  G
For compassion so ama - zing.
         G/B      C2      Dsus4    G/B        C2
Lord, we come to give You thanks for all You've done.
```

Chorus:
```
            G/B C2 Dsus4       G/B C2 Dsus4
Because of Your love    -       we're forgiven.
               G/B C2 Dsus4          G/B C2 Dsus4
Because of Your love    -       our hearts are clean.
            G/B C2 Dsus4          G/B C2 Dsus4
We lift You up      -       with songs of freedom,
         C2          D
Forever we're changed  -  because of Your love.
G/B    C2    Dsus4  G
         (Hey, hey, hey!)
G/B    C2    Dsus4  G
         (Hey, hey!)
```

Mid section:
```
G/B         C      D       G
   You're the One who has given us freedom,
G/B         C      D       G
   You're the One who is making us new.
G/B         C      D       G
   You're the One who is bringing us healing.
G/B         C    D
   We owe it all to You
```

Taken from
BECAUSE OF YOUR LOVE
Brenton Brown
SURCD5124

A THOUSAND TIMES I'VE FAILED

From the inside out

Joel Houston

F   C   G   Am F2 Dm9 Dm7

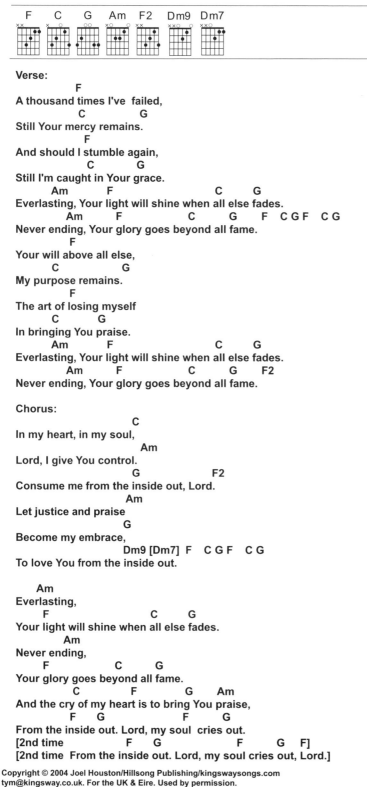

Verse:
       F
A thousand times I've failed,
      C   G
Still Your mercy remains.
        F
And should I stumble again,
      C   G
Still I'm caught in Your grace.
    Am   F   C   G
Everlasting, Your light will shine when all else fades.
       Am   F   C   G   F C G F C G
Never ending, Your glory goes beyond all fame.
      F
Your will above all else,
    C   G
My purpose remains.
      F
The art of losing myself
    C   G
In bringing You praise.
    Am   F   C   G
Everlasting, Your light will shine when all else fades.
       Am   F   C   G   F2
Never ending, Your glory goes beyond all fame.

Chorus:
               C
In my heart, in my soul,
                Am
Lord, I give You control.
           G   F2
Consume me from the inside out, Lord.
          Am
Let justice and praise
          G
Become my embrace,
         Dm9 [Dm7] F   C G F   C G
To love You from the inside out.

   Am
Everlasting,
    F   C   G
Your light will shine when all else fades.
     Am
Never ending,
    F   C   G
Your glory goes beyond all fame.
        C   F   G   Am
And the cry of my heart is to bring You praise,
      F   G   F   G
From the inside out. Lord, my soul cries out.
[2nd time   F   G   F   G F]
[2nd time From the inside out. Lord, my soul cries out, Lord.]

Taken from
LOVE CAME DOWN
Soul Survivor Live 2006
SURCD5076

AT THE START, HE WAS THERE

The glory of it all

David Crowder

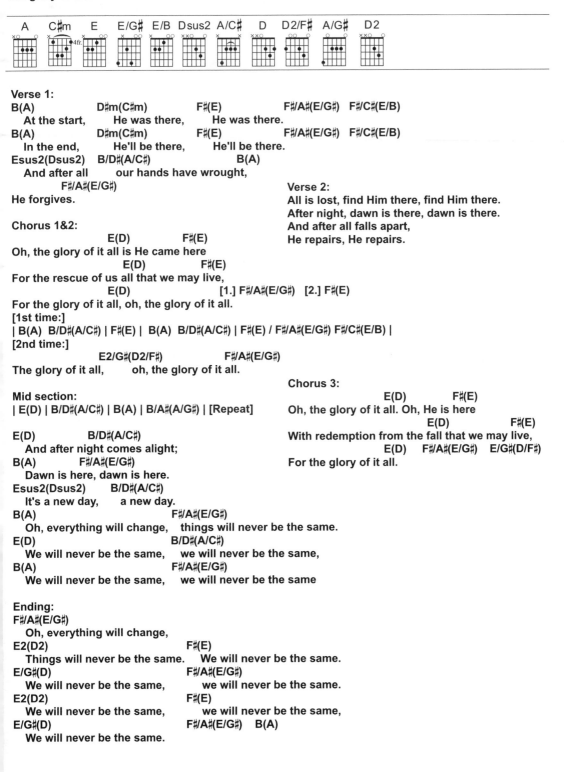

A C#m E E/G# E/B Dsus2 A/C# D D2/F# A/G# D2

Verse 1:
B(A)   D#m(C#m)   F#(E)   F#/A#(E/G#) F#/C#(E/B)
  At the start,   He was there,   He was there.
B(A)   D#m(C#m)   F#(E)   F#/A#(E/G#) F#/C#(E/B)
  In the end,   He'll be there,   He'll be there.
Esus2(Dsus2) B/D#(A/C#)   B(A)
  And after all   our hands have wrought,
        F#/A#(E/G#)
He forgives.

Chorus 1&2:
                    E(D)   F#(E)
Oh, the glory of it all is He came here
                    E(D)   F#(E)
For the rescue of us all that we may live,
                    E(D)   [1.] F#/A#(E/G#) [2.] F#(E)
For the glory of it all, oh, the glory of it all.
[1st time:]
| B(A) B/D#(A/C#) | F#(E) | B(A) B/D#(A/C#) | F#(E) / F#/A#(E/G#) F#/C#(E/B) |
[2nd time:]
                    E2/G#(D2/F#)   F#/A#(E/G#)
The glory of it all,   oh, the glory of it all.

Verse 2:
All is lost, find Him there, find Him there.
After night, dawn is there, dawn is there.
And after all falls apart,
He repairs, He repairs.

Mid section:
| E(D) | B/D#(A/C#) | B(A) | B/A#(A/G#) | [Repeat]

E(D)   B/D#(A/C#)
  And after night comes alight;
B(A)   F#/A#(E/G#)
  Dawn is here, dawn is here.
Esus2(Dsus2)   B/D#(A/C#)
  It's a new day,   a new day.
B(A)   F#/A#(E/G#)
  Oh, everything will change,   things will never be the same.
E(D)   B/D#(A/C#)
  We will never be the same,   we will never be the same,
B(A)   F#/A#(E/G#)
  We will never be the same,   we will never be the same

Chorus 3:
                                  E(D)   F#(E)
Oh, the glory of it all. Oh, He is here
                                  E(D)   F#(E)
With redemption from the fall that we may live,
                                  E(D)   F#/A#(E/G#) E/G#(D/F#)
For the glory of it all.

Ending:
F#/A#(E/G#)
  Oh, everything will change,
E2(D2)   F#(E)
  Things will never be the same.   We will never be the same.
E/G#(D)   F#/A#(E/G#)
  We will never be the same,   we will never be the same.
E2(D2)   F#(E)
  We will never be the same,   we will never be the same,
E/G#(D)   F#/A#(E/G#) B(A)
  We will never be the same.

Taken from
REMEDY
David Crowder Band
SURCD5101

AWAKE, MY GOD, AND MOVE

(Justice be my light)

Claire Hamilton
& Johnny Parks

G2 Asus2+4 D6   Bm7 Em7+4

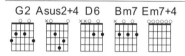

Verse:
```
 G2               Asus2+4           D6
Awake, my God,        and move,
 Bm7        G2         Em7+4
Let  mercy flood my heart.
 G2               Asus2+4          D6
Awake and speak       Your truth;
 Bm7     G2        Em7+4
Let justice be my light.
```

```
        Bm7       G2
We will love mercy,
            D6
We will act   justly,
         Bm7        G2          D6
We will walk humbly before You, Lord.
         Bm7      G2
We will love mercy,
            D6
We will act   justly,
         Bm7            G2          D6
We will walk humbly before You, Lord.
```

```
 Bm7       G2         D6
Let Jesus be my light.
 Bm7       G2         D6
Let justice be my light.
 Bm7       G2         D6
Let Jesus be my light.
```

BEAUTY UNSPOKEN

Paul Oakley

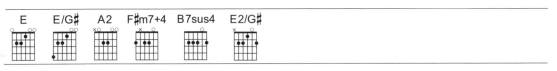

E   E/G♯   A2   F♯m7+4   B7sus4   E2/G♯

Verse 1:
```
         E                 E/G♯
```
Beauty unspoken, glory unchanging,
```
A2
```
Maker of the stars above.
```
         E                 E/G♯
```
God uncreated, made Yourself nothing;
```
A2
```
Carrying the cross for love.

Chorus:
```
A    E/G♯   F♯m7+4
```
Thank You, God,
```
A    E/G♯   F♯m7+4
```
Thank You, God,
```
A    E/G♯   B7sus4        E
```
Thank You, God, for saving me.

Verse 2:
Light in the darkness, One with the Father.
The Beginning and the End.
Lifter of burdens, bruised and forsaken,
Jesus Christ - the sinner's Friend.

Bridge:
```
         E
```
You are love never ending,
```
    E2/G♯      E/G♯
```
Your grace, overwhelming;
```
  A           B7sus4
```
Crucified for me.
```
         E
```
And this blood never failing,
```
    E2/G♯     E/G♯
```
Your mercy unveiling,
```
  A           B7sus4
```
Given, Lord, for me.   **[Repeat]**

Taken from
LET THE RAIN COME
Newday Live
SURCD5112

BEFORE CREATION'S TIME

(Breathe)

Andy Smith

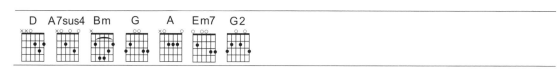

Verse 1:
D
  Before creation's time

Majestically You reign,
A7sus4
  You patent Your design

On all that You have made.
Bm   G   D   A7sus4
  Creator God, breathe life in us.

Verse 2:
We took eternal life
And traded it for dust,
Your perfect sacrifice
Has bought it back for us;
You hold salvation in Your hands.

Chorus:
D   A
  You turned my ashes into beauty,
                      G
Turned my sorrow into joy.
            D   A7sus4
Breathe life, breathe life.
D   A
  You take these dry bones, make them stand,
                G
Put a promise in my hand.
            D   A7sus4 [D to end]
Breathe life, breathe life.

Verse 3:
The idols of this world
Will fade to shades of grey,
When marked against the One
Who is the only way,
Bright shining sun that lights my path.

Mid section:
Em7   G2   A7sus4
  Wonderful, marvellous, You make all things new.
Em7   G2   A7sus4
  I was dead, now I'm alive all because of You.
Em7   G   A7sus4   G A7sus4
  So I will go and tell the world how great You are.

Taken from
BREATHE
Andy Smith
SURCD5073

BEFORE THE DAY

(Made to worship)

Chris Tomlin, Stephen Sharp
& Ed Cash

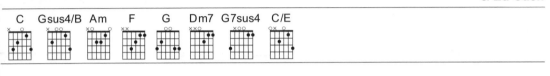

C Gsus4/B Am F G Dm7 G7sus4 C/E

Verse 1:
```
    C                   Gsus4/B
Before the day, before the light,
    Am                                F   G
Before the world revolved around the sun,
C                       Gsus4/B
God on high stepped down into time,
          Am                     F   G
And wrote the story of His love for everyone.
```

Bridge:
```
F                   G
   He has filled our hearts with wonder,
F            C/G      F
   So that we always remember:
```

Chorus:
```
C
You and I are made to worship,
F
You and I are called to love,
Dm7                     G7sus4
You and I are forgiven and free.
          C
When you and I embrace surrender,
        F
When you and I choose to believe,
        Dm7             G
Then you and I will see
                      [1.3.C]  [2.Dm7]
Who we  are meant to be.
```

Verse 2:
All we are, and all we have,
Is all a gift from God that we receive.
Brought to life, we open up our eyes,
To see the majesty and glory of the King.

Mid section
```
                  C/E
Even the rocks cry out,
                       F
Even the heavens shout,
              G
At the sound of His holy name.
Dm7                    C/E
   So let every voice sing out,
                         F
Let every knee bow down,
          G
He's worthy of all our praise.
```

CAN YOU FEEL IT?

David Crowder, Patrick Dodd,
Jeremy Bush & Mike Dodson

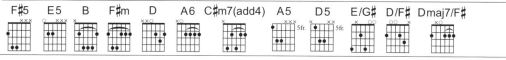

F♯5 E5 B F♯m D A6 C♯m7(add4) A5 D5 E/G♯ D/F♯ Dmaj7/F♯

Chorus 1 & 2:
　　　F♯5
Can you feel it, can you feel it?
　E5　　　　　　　　　　　B
The love in this place - can you feel it?
　　　　F♯5
Can you feel it, can you feel it?
　E5　　　　　　　　　　B　　　　F♯5
The grace in this place - can you feel it? Yeah.

Verse:
F♯m
Life makes it so hard sometimes
D
　To know what's real.
F♯m
Life makes it so hard sometimes
D
　To know what's real.
　　　　　F♯m
Oh this life makes it so hard sometimes
D
　To know what's real.
F♯m　　　　　　　　　　A6　　C♯m7(add4)
Life makes it so hard sometimes.

Mid Section:
F♯5　　　　　E5　　F♯5
　When I can't feel You there,
A5　　　　　B5　　F♯5　E5
　When I can't see You there,
D5　　　B5　　　　　　　　F♯5
　When I can't comprehend that You are there
E5　　　　　　　　　D5　　　　E5
You are there. You're everywhere.
　　　　　B5
You are everywhere.

Ending:
| D | E/G♯ | D/F♯ | E | D| E/G♯ |
D/F♯　　　　　　E
　Our God is here.
D　　　E　　　　Dmaj7/F♯　E/G♯
　Our God is here.
D　　　E　　　　Dmaj7/F♯　E/G♯
　Our God is here.
F♯5
　We believe You're here.
A5　　　B5　　　F♯5　E5
　We can feel You here.
D5　　　B5　　　F♯5　E5
　We can see You here.
D5　　　E5　　　F♯5　A5　　　B5　　　　F♯5
　We believe You're here.　　You are here, You are here.

Chorus 3:
Can you feel it, can you feel it?
The hope in this place - can you feel it?
Can you feel it, can you feel it?
The peace in this place - can you feel it?

Taken from
REMEDY
David Crowder Band
SURCD5101

COME, LET US RETURN TO THE LORD 17.

Gloria

Brenton Brown & Matt Maher

Verse 1:

C   G   G7
Come, let us return to the Lord.
C   G   G7
Come, let us return to the Lord.
C   Em   D
Fill this room with sound, let the praise resound.
C   G
Come, Let us return to the Lord.

Come, let us return to the Lord.
Come, let us return to the Lord.
Let's fill this room with sound, the praise of God resound.
Come, Let us return to the Lord.

Chorus:

    C   G
Gloria, gloria,
        D   Em
Lord, our eyes are fixed upon You.
    C   G
Gloria, gloria,
        D   C   G
Turn our hearts to You again.

Verse 2:
Welcomed to the table of the King.
Welcomed to the table of the King.
Homeless and ashamed,
The Saviour called our names.
We've been welcomed to the table of the King.

Mid section:

                    Am
Look what You've done,
                    Em
Look what You've done.
        D   G
All that we have is Yours alone.
               Am
What can we give?
     Em
What offering?
       D   C
You deserve more than the songs we sing.

Verse 3:
So let mercy rise like praise to Your throne.
Let mercy rise like praise to Your throne.
Father, touch Your church
'Til justice fills the earth.
Let mercy rise like praise to Your throne.

Taken from
BECAUSE OF YOUR LOVE
Brenton Brown
SURCD5124

CREATOR, SUSTAINER

Wonderful

Brenton Brown & Doug Bacon

G   D   Em   C   D/F#   Csus2

Capo 4(G)

Verse 1:
B(G)   F#(D)   G#m(Em)   E(C)
 Creator,   sustainer,   our hearts were made for You.
B(G)   F#(D)   G#m(Em)   E(C)
 Our Abba,   our Father,   the home we're running to.

Bridge:
F#/A#(D/F#)   E(C)   F#/A#(D/F#)   E(C)
 Drawn by Your kindness,   held by Your grace.
F#/A#(D/F#)   E(C)   G#m(Em) F#(D)   E(C)
 Your generous mercy inspires   songs of praise. Yeah.

Chorus 1:
        B(G)   F#(D)   G#m(Em)   E(C)
Wonderful, wonderful, You're the one thing that we need.
        B(G)   F#(D)   G#m(Em)   Esus2(Csus2)
How we long for Your house, for the healing that it brings.

Verse 2:
Protector, provider, the God who calls us friend.
Our shepherd, our shelter, we turn to You again.

Chorus 2:
        B(G)   F#(D)   G#m(Em)   E(C)
Wonderful, wonderful, You're the one thing that we need.
        B(G)   F#(D)   G#m(Em)   E(C)
How we long for Your house, for the healing that it brings.
        B(G)   F#(D)   G#m(Em)   E(C)
Beautiful, beautiful, more than any other thing.
        B(G)   F#(D)   G#m(Em)   E(C)
We were born for Your courts, for the presence of the King. Yeah.

Mid section:
B(G)   F#(D)   G#m(Em) E(C)
 You're all we need, Lord Jesus, our hearts were made for You.
B(G)   F#(D)   G#m(Em) E(C)
 You're all we need, Lord Jesus, no other God will do.
Mid section:
B(G)   F#(D)   G#m(Em) E(C)
 You're all we need, Lord Jesus, our hearts were made for You.
B(G)   F#(D)   G#m(Em) E(C)
 You're all we need, Lord Jesus,   Jesus.

Taken from
BECAUSE OF YOUR LOVE
Brenton Brown
SURCD5124

DEFENDER OF THIS HEART

Remain

Ben Cantelon

Verse 1:
D   A
  Defender of this heart,
                   Bm
You loved me from the start,
      G
  You never change.
D   A
  Through the highs and lows,
            Bm
As seasons come and go,
     G
You never fail.
          D
Day after day,
   A   Bm
Your love will remain,
G   D   A
Faithful and true, You are good.

Verse 2:
When troubles come my way,
You guide and You sustain;
Lead me, I pray.
Forever You will be
The great eternal King,
Now and always.
Day after day,
Your love will remain,
Faithful and true, You are good.

Chorus:
            G   D/G   A
You are God with us, You're victorious,
D/G   G   D/G   A
You are strong and mighty to save.
           G
For Your word stands true,
D/G   A
There is none like You,
D/G   G   D/G   A
And when all else fades You remain.   [Repeat]

Ending:
| Em | G | D | A | Em | G | D | A | D ||

Taken from
DAYLIGHT BREAKS THROUGH
Ben Cantelon
SURCD5094

DESPERATE TO SEE YOUR GLORY

(We see Your glory)

Ian Yates

Bm7   G   D

Capo 2

Verse 1:
Bm7   G
Desperate to see Your glory,
        D
We're desperate to see You move,
Bm7   G   D
Come and change this broken land, O God.

Verse 2:
We're living for Your glory,
We're living to see You move,
Come and change this broken land, O God.

Chorus:
      Bm7   G
We're desperate to see Your glory,
      D
We're desperate to see You move,
        Bm7   G   D
We're desperate to see Your kingdom on the earth. [Repeat]

Verse 3:
We're waiting for Your glory,
We know that day will come,
When the glory of
Our God will fall on us.

Coda 1:
D   Bm7   G
Never to be the same, we long for the cloud,
D
   We long for the fire,
      Bm7   G   D
We're longing for Your rain on heaven on earth.

Taken from
THE PEOPLE'S ALBUM, 3,
SURCD5140

DRAW NEAR TO US

Johnny Parks & Claire Hamilton

D   A/C♯   Bm   G   A

Chorus:
D   A/C♯
  Draw near to us,
      Bm
Draw near to us,
       G   A   D
As we draw near to You. [Repeat]

Verse:
       G   D   A
You make whole those who come in Your name;
Bm   G   D   A
  You lift up those who live in Your light.
Bm   G   D   A
  As You rise, as You move, we are changed.
      Bm   G   A
By Your grace, will You bring us near?

EVEN THOUGH I WALK

You never let go

Matt & Beth Redman

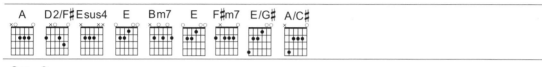

A   D2/F♯ Esus4   E   Bm7   E   F♯m7   E/G♯ A/C♯

Capo 2
Verse 1:
              A
Even though I walk through the valley of the shadow of death,
     D2/F♯
Your perfect love is casting out fear.
                A
And even when I'm caught in the middle of the storms of this life,
  D2/F♯   [Esus4   E to end]
I won't turn back, I know You are near.
           F♯m   E   A   D E A
And I will fear no e   -   vil, for my God is with me.
          D E A   Esus4
And if my God is with me, whom then shall I fear,
E   D
Whom then shall I fear?

Chorus:
A
O no, You never let go,

Through the calm and through the storm.
F♯m7
O no, You never let go,

In every high and every low.
Esus4
O no, You never let go,
D2   A   E D
Lord, You never let go of me.

Verse 2:
And I can see a light that is coming
For the heart that holds on
A glorious light beyond all compare.
And there will be an end to these troubles,
But until that day comes we'll live
To know you here on the earth.
And I will fear no evil . . .

Bridge:
           A
Yes, I can see a light that is coming

For the heart that holds on,
              F♯m
And there will be an end to these troubles,

But until that day comes,
E
Still I will praise You,
D   A   E D
Still I will praise You.

Yes, I can see a . . .

Taken from
BEAUTIFUL NEWS
Matt Redman
SURCD5071

EVERYBODY DANCE

All Your saints

Matt Redman

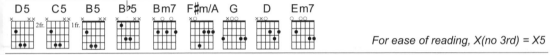

D5 C5 B5 B♭5 Bm7 F♯m/A G D Em7

For ease of reading, X(no 3rd) = X5

Capo 2

Chorus 1:

      E5(D5) D5(C5) C#5(B5) C(B♭5)
Everybody dance,
      E5(D5)   D5(C5) C#5(B5) C(B♭5)
Everybody dance for joy!
      E5(D5) D5(C5) C#5(B5) C(B♭5)
Everybody shout,
      E5(D5)   D5(C5) C#5(B5) C(B♭5)
Everybody make some noise!
[Last time only:]
      E5(D5)
Make some noise.

Verse 1:
C#m7(Bm7)   G#m/B(F#m/A)
  Start up a song and   let it be known that
A(G)
Mercy has come, mercy has come.
C#m7(Bm7)   G#m/B(F#m/A)
  Strike up the band and   let it be told that
A(G)
Rescue is here, rescue is here.

Verse 2:
Here at the cross the theme of our song is
Kindness and love, kindness and love.
Justice was done there, freedom was won and
You saved the day, You saved the day.

Bridge:
C#m7(Bm7)   G#m/B(F#m/A)
Someone turn the lights up,
A(G)
Someone play the music louder now.
C#m7(Bm7)   G#m/B(F#m/A)
Come on, tell the whole world:
      A(G)   F#m(Em)
There's a God who saves, there's a God who saves, there's a God who saves

Chorus 2:
      E(D)   A(G)
Our hearts arise to sing Your song,
F#m7(Em7)   E(D)
  And all Your saints go dancing, dancing on.
      E(D)   A(G)
Through darkest night till break of dawn,
F#m7(Em7)   E(D)
  All Your saints go dancing, dancing on.

Mid section:
C5(B♭5)   C#m7(Bm7)
Everybody dance,
B(A)   A(G)
Everybody dance for joy!
      C#m7(Bm7)
Everybody shout,
B(A)   D(C)
Everybody make some noise!

Taken from
LET THE RAIN COME
Newday Live
SURCD5109

EVERYONE NEEDS COMPASSION

Mighty to save

Reuben Morgan & Ben Fielding

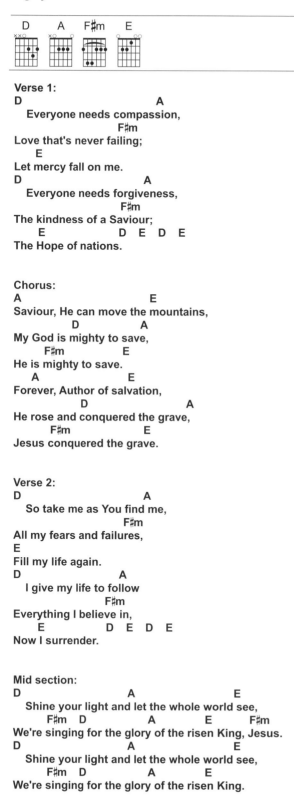

```
D        A     F#m    E
```

Verse 1:
```
D                        A
   Everyone needs compassion,
               F#m
Love that's never failing;
     E
Let mercy fall on me.
D                        A
   Everyone needs forgiveness,
                  F#m
The kindness of a Saviour;
     E          D  E  D  E
The Hope of nations.
```

Chorus:
```
A                        E
Saviour, He can move the mountains,
           D           A
My God is mighty to save,
     F#m          E
He is mighty to save.
     A              E
Forever, Author of salvation,
              D            A
He rose and conquered the grave,
     F#m               E
Jesus conquered the grave.
```

Verse 2:
```
D                        A
   So take me as You find me,
                   F#m
All my fears and failures,
E
Fill my life again.
D                  A
   I give my life to follow
                 F#m
Everything I believe in,
     E          D  E  D  E
Now I surrender.
```

Mid section:
```
D                A                E
   Shine your light and let the whole world see,
       F#m  D          A       E     F#m
We're singing for the glory of the risen King, Jesus.
D                A                E
   Shine your light and let the whole world see,
       F#m  D          A       E
We're singing for the glory of the risen King.
```

Taken from
LIVING FOR YOUR GLORY
Soul Survivor Live 2007
SURCD5108
and
LET THE RAIN COME
Newday Live
SURCD5109

FATHER, HOLD ME
(Over me)

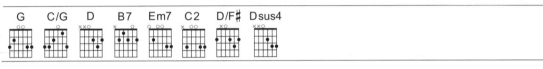

G   C/G   D   B7   Em7   C2   D/F♯   Dsus4

Capo 3

Verse 1:
G   C/G   G
   Father, hold me like a new born child.
D   G
   Father, hold me like a new born child.
     B7   Em7 D   C2
Father, calm me when I run wild,
G   D   G
Father, watch over me.

Verse 2:
Father, cool me when the fever's high,
Father, cool me when the fever's high,
Father, show me through Jesus' eyes,
And Father, watch over me.

Chorus:
    C   G
Over me, like the rain come down.
    D   G
Over me, how sweet the sound.
    C   G D/F♯   Em7
Over me, angels gathered round.
C2   Dsus4   G
Father, watch over me.

[Last time:]
C2   Dsus4   G C/G   G
Father, watch over me.

Verse 3:
Father, call me to Your loving side,
Father, call me to Your loving side,
Father, speak to me and I'll be alright,
And Father, watch over me.

Taken from
SEE THE MORNING
Chris Tomlin
SURCD5084

FATHER OF EVERLASTING GRACE

(My soul is complete)

Phil Shaw

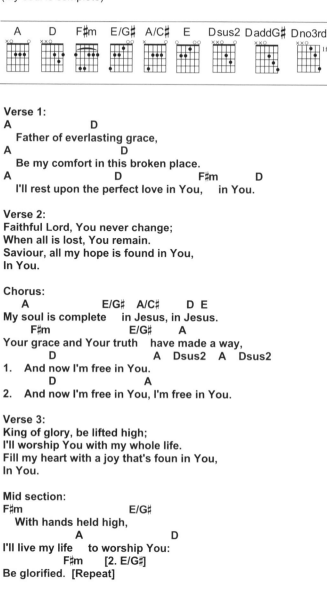

A   D   F♯m   E/G♯   A/C♯   E   Dsus2 DaddG♯ Dno3rd

Verse 1:

A   D
  Father of everlasting grace,
A   D
  Be my comfort in this broken place.
A   D   F♯m   D
  I'll rest upon the perfect love in You,   in You.

Verse 2:

Faithful Lord, You never change;
When all is lost, You remain.
Saviour, all my hope is found in You,
In You.

Chorus:

  A   E/G♯ A/C♯   D E
My soul is complete   in Jesus, in Jesus.
     F♯m   E/G♯   A
Your grace and Your truth   have made a way,
      D   A Dsus2 A Dsus2
1. And now I'm free in You.
        D   A
2. And now I'm free in You, I'm free in You.

Verse 3:

King of glory, be lifted high;
I'll worship You with my whole life.
Fill my heart with a joy that's foun in You,
In You.

Mid section:

F♯m   E/G♯
  With hands held high,
          A   D
I'll live my life   to worship You:
       F♯m   [2. E/G♯]
Be glorified. [Repeat]

Coda:

D   E   D   DaddG♯ [ad lib] Dno3rd
Now I'm free in You.

Taken from
THE PEOPLE'S ALBUM, 3,
SURCD5140

FILL MY CUP

Paul Baloche, Steven Curtis-Chapman, Stuart Garrard,Israel Houghton,
Tim Hughes, Graham Kendrick,Andy Park, Matt Redman,
Martin Smith, Michael W. Smith, Chris Tomlin, Darlene Zschech

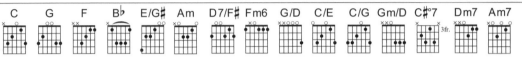

C   G   F   B♭   E/G♯   Am   D7/F♯   Fm6   G/D   C/E   C/G   Gm/D   C♯°7   Dm7   Am7

Verse 1:
C   G
Fill my cup so it's overflowing,
      F   C
Flowing like a river, fill my cup.
                      G
Fill my cup, fill it with Your mercies,
                F   C
Love and truth and justice, fill my cup.

Chorus 1 only:
B♭   E/G♯
Oh Lord, the river's running high,
   Am   G   F
So take me to the other side.
B♭   E/G♯
Oh Lord, the tide's running high,
   Am   G   D7/F♯   Fm6   [1.C]
So take me to the other side.   (woah.)

Verse 2:
Fill my cup, so it's overflowing,
Flowing like a river, fill my cup.
Take this cup, heavy with your blessing,
Pour it over nations, take this cup.

Chorus 2:
B♭   E/G♯
Oh Lord, the river's running high,
   Am   G   F
So take me to the other side.
B♭   E/G♯
Oh Lord, the flood's running high,
   Am   G   D7/F♯   Fm6   [1.C]
So take me to the other side.   (woah.)

Mid section:
C   G/D   C/E
Rivers of living water
F   C/G   E7/G♯   Am
Overflowing through me
Gm/D C♯°7 Dm7   C/E F
From the throne of God,
E/G♯ Am7   C/G   C
Overflowing through me. [Repeat x3]

Tag
C   G
Take us to the other side,
B♭/F   F   C
Take us to the other side. [Repeat x8]

Taken from
COMPASSIONART

FOR EVERY SONG

You are

Ben Cantelon

G   Gsus4   Em   C   Am7   Em7   D   Dadd4

Capo 3

Verse 1:
```
         Bb(G)  Bbsus4(Gsus4)  Bb(G)  Bbsus4(Gsus4)
For every song,        for every breath,
         Gm(Em)        Eb(C)       Bb(G)   Bbsus4(Gsus4)
For every good and perfect gift You give.
         Bb(G)  Bbsus4(Gsus4)  Bb(G)  Bbsus4(Gsus4)
For every night,        for every day,
         Gm(Em)        Eb(C)     Bb(G)   Bbsus4(Gsus4)
For the glory of the earth,   we will say:
```

Chorus:
```
         Bb(G)      Cm7(Am7)
You are    over everything,
         Gm7(Em7) Eb(C)
You are      the eternal King.
         Bb(G)          Cm7(Am7)
Jesus,      You're the song we sing;
         Gm7(Em7)        Eb(C)   [Last time: Bb(G)]
You are, You are, You are.
```

Verse 2:
For Your word, full of grace,
For all the steadfast promises You make.
For the cross, for new life,
For the beauty of Your sacrifice.

Mid section:
```
         Eb(C)
You will always be,
         F(D)
You will always be,
         Gm7(Em7)          Fadd4(Dadd4)
You will always be the great I Am.
         Eb(C)
You will always be,
         F(D)
You will always be,
         Gm7(Em7)          Fadd4(Dadd4)
You will always be the great I Am.
```

Taken from
DAYLIGHT BREAKS THROUGH
Ben Cantelon
SURCD5094
and
LIVING FOR YOUR GLORY
Soul Survivor Live 2007
SURCD5108

FREEDOM IS COMING

Freedom

Johnny Parks & Claire Hamilton

G D C Em Em/D G/D G/B

Verse 1:
G
Freedom is coming, freedom is here.
D
Shake off your worries, lay down your fears.
G
Join in the anthem, join in the song.
D
Dance in the freedom of victory won.
C
No more sadness, there is joy.
Em
No more anguish, there is peace.
C
Bring your burdens, bring your fears.
D   Em/D D Em/D D G/D D
Bring them in - to   glorious freedom!

Chorus:
G/B   C   Em   D
Christ has done enough to set us free.
G/B   C   Em   D   G   D   [G]
We will live a life that's been redeemed.

Verse 2:
Once we were captive, now we are free,
Shame cannot grip us, we've been redeemed.
Hope is His message, hope in our hearts:
The King of our freedom has paid the great cost.
No more sorrow - there is comfort.
No more heartache - there is healing.
Bring your burdens, bring your fears,
Bring them into glorious freedom!

Taken from
BREAK THE SILENCE
Johnny Parks Band
SURCD5095

GOD, AS WE WALK THIS WORLD

Walk the world

Charlie Hall & Kendall Combes

Am   D   Em7   C2   Em   G   C

Capo 4(G)

Verse 1:
C#m(Am) F#(D) G#m7(Em7) E2(C2)
 God,   as we walk this   world,
C#m(Am) F#(D)   G#m(Em)
 We   want to be a sign.
C#m(Am) F#(D)   G#m7(Em7) E2(C2)
 Our   prayers flow into   love,
C#m(Am) F#(D)   G#m(Em)
 Giv - ing Your life.
C#m(Am)
 Broken but singing,
F#(D)
 Our hearts keep shining.

Chorus:
B(G)
 Let my life shine, come and let my heart shine,
G#m7(Em7)
 We're gonna walk the world,
E(C)
 Lift the bread and wine.
C#m(Am)
 Like the stars shine, come and let our hearts shine.
E(C)   [Last time:] B(G)
 In a dark world, we lift the bread and wine.

Link to verse 2:
| C#m(Am) F#(D) | G#m7(Em7) E2(C2) | C#m(Am) F#(D) | G#m7(Em7) |

Verse 2:
And we were born for this:
Born for this day and time.
Our prayers flow into love,
Giving our lives.
Broken but singing,
Our hearts keep shining.

Mid section:
| C#m(Am) | C#m(Am) | F#(D) | F#(D) |
C#m(Am)
 Broken but singing,
F#(D)
 Our hearts keep shining.
C#m(Am)
 Broken but singing,
F#(D)
 Our hearts keep shining.

Taken from
GOD OF THIS CITY
Passion
SURCD5126

GOD CAME DOWN
(Great is Your glory)

Vicky Beeching
& Ed Cash

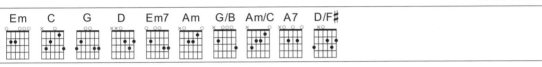

Em   C   G   D   Em7   Am   G/B   Am/C   A7   D/F#

Verse 1:
Em   C
God came down and gave His life for me,
  G   D
Amen, amen.
          Em   C
Through flesh and blood He fought for victory,
  G   D
Amen, amen.
Em   C
Crucified, brought back to life,
  G   D
Amen, amen.
Em   C
Seated at the Father's hand again,
  G   D
Amen, amen.

Chorus:
G   Am   G/B   Am/C
Great is the glory of the Lord Almighty.
G   Am   G/B   Am/C
Great is the glory of the Lord.
        G   A7   G/B   Am/C
I will sing with all my heart unto the Lord Almighty.
G   D   G
Great is Your glory, Lord.

Mid section:
G
You are the One who was,
                  D/F#
You are the One who is,
                    Em7   C
You are the One who is to come.
                          G
You are the One who was,
                  D/F#
You are the One who is,
                    Em7   C
You are the One who is to come.

Verse 2:
Crimson covered over sinless hands,
Amen, amen.
But nails could never hold the Son of Man,
Amen, amen.
Now the Father's love flows down on us,
Amen, amen.
Hallelujah, He will come again,
Amen amen.

Taken from
PAINTING THE
INVISIBLE
SURCD5091

GOD, YOU HAVE DONE GREAT THINGS

(Let Your mercy rain)

Chris Tomlin, Ed Cash
& Jesse Reeves

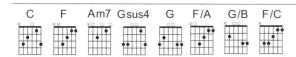

Verse:
C   F   C
God, You have done great things,
     F   C
God, You give grace to the weak
     F   Am7
And bless the brokenhearted
          G
With a song of praise to sing.
            F   C
You reached down and lifted us up,
        F   C
You came running, looking for us.
             F
And now there's nothing,
     Am7   Gsus4   G
And no one beyond Your love.

Chorus:
          C
You're the overflow,
       F
You're the fountain of my heart.
F/A   G
So let Your mercy rain,
      F   C
Let Your mercy rain on us.
         C
You're the faithful One,
       F
When the world's falling apart.
F/A   G
So let Your mercy rain,
       F   C
Let Your mercy rain on us.

      Am7   G/B
How deep, how wide,
     C   F
How long, how high
      C   F   C F
Is Your love, is Your love. [Repeat] O God.

      C
You're the overflow,
      F
You're the fountain of my heart,
       G
So let Your mercy rain,
      F   C
Let Your mercy rain on us.

Last chorus:
           G
You're the overflow,
       F
You're the fountain of my heart.
F/A   G
So let Your mercy rain,
       F   C
Let Your mercy rain on us.
          C
You're the faithful One,
       F
When the world's falling apart.
F/A   G
So let Your mercy rain,
       F   F/C C F/C C
Let Your mercy rain   on us.
           F/C C F/C C
Let it rain.

Taken from
SEE THE MORNING
Chris Tomlin
SURCD5084

GREAT IS THE LORD

Chris Sayburn

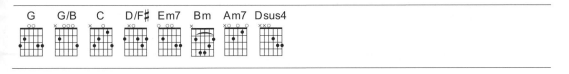

G   G/B   C   D/F♯   Em7   Bm   Am7   Dsus4

Capo 4

Verse 1:
G   G/B   C   D/F♯
Great is the Lord and most worthy of praise,
G   G/B   C
Who can compare to His greatness?
　Em7   D/F♯   Bm   C
Creation displays in magnificent ways
　Am7   G/B   C
His glory, His majesty, His splendour.

Chorus:
G   D/F♯
Great is the Father, great is the Son,
Em7   C
Great is the Spirit, great is the Three in One;
　　Em7   D/F♯
Singing great is the Lord.
G   D/F♯
Great in his mercy, great in His love,
Em7   C
Great in his power, great in His fullness above,
　　Em7   D/F♯ [1. G G/B   C]
Singing great is the Lord.

Verse 2:
Great is the Lord and most worthy of praise;
Who can determine His greatness?
The heavens display in extravagant ways
Your glory, your majesty, Your splendour.

Mid section:
　　C   D/F♯
How marvellous, how glorious You are.
　　C   Dsus4
How powerful, how merciful You are. [Repeat]

Coda:
　　C   D/F♯
Singing great is the Lord,
　　C   D/F♯ G
Singing great is the Lord.

Taken from
THE PEOPLE'S ALBUM, 3,
SURCD5140

HALLELUJAH, HALLELUJAH

Hallelujah

Ben Cantelon

Em   C   G   D/F#

Capo 2

Chorus:
    F#m(Em) D(C)   A(G)   E/G#(D/F#)
Hallelujah,   hallelujah,
      F#m(Em) D(C)   A(G)   E/G#(D/F#)
You are worthy   of our praise.
    F#m(Em) D(C)   A(G)   E/G#(D/F#)
Hallelujah,   hallelujah,
      F#m(Em) D(C)   A(G)   E/G#(D/F#)
You are worthy   of our praise.

Verse:
F#m(Em)
  Be high and lifted up,
D(C)
  Be high and lifted up,
A(G)   E/G#(D/F#)
  Be high and lifted up, Jesus.
F#m(Em)
  It's You we glorify,
D(C)
  It's You we're lifting high.
A(G)   E/G#(D/F#)
  Your name be glorified.

Taken from
LIVING FOR YOUR GLORY
Soul Survivor Live 2007
SURCD5108

HEAR THE HOLY ROAR OF GOD RESOUND   35.

(Let God arise)

Chris Tomlin, Ed Cash
& Jesse Reeves

A5/G   A5   F#m7   E   D5   A/G   A   D/G   D/A   A7/G   A7   Em/G   Asus4/D   A5/E

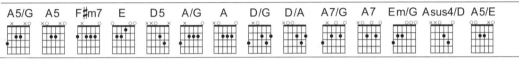

For ease or reading A(no3rd) = A5

Capo 2

Verse 1:
       A5/G A5   A5/G A5
Hear the holy   roar of God resound,
       A5/G   A5   A5/G A5
Watch the waters part before us now,
            F#m7
Come and see what He has done for us,
  E
Tell the world of His great love.

Bridge:
     D5   F#m7   E
Our God is a God who saves,
     D5   F#m7   E
Our God is a God who saves;

Chorus:
       A/G A   D/G   D/A
Let God arise,   let God arise.
         A7/G   A7
Our God reigns   now and forever,
    D/G   D/A   [1.Em/G A D   Em/G A D]
He reigns now and forever. [2. To chorus]
                [3.Asus4/D   F#m7 A5/E x2]
                [4.Em/G A D x2 A5]

Verse 2:
His enemies will run for sure,
The church will stand, she will endure.
He holds the keys of life, our Lord,
Death has no sting, no final word.

Taken from
SEE THE MORNING
Chris Tomlin
SURCD5084

HEAR THE HOLY ROAR OF GOD RESOUND   35.

(Let God arise)

Chris Tomlin, Ed Cash
& Jesse Reeves

For ease or reading B(no3rd) = B5

Verse 1:
```
          B5/A  B5                 B5/A  B5
Hear the holy    roar of God resound,
          B5/A   B5               B5/A  B5
Watch the waters part before us now,
        G#m7
Come and see what He has done for us,
   F#
Tell the world of His great love.
```

Bridge:
```
        E5        G#m7         F#
Our God  is a God who saves,
        E5        G#m7         F#
Our God is a God who saves;
```

Chorus:
```
           B/A   B              E/A   E/B
Let God arise,       let God arise.
                 B7/A      B7
Our God reigns    now and forever,
       E/A   E/B          [1.F#m/A  B  E  F#m/A  B  E]
He reigns now and forever. [2. To chorus]
                          [3.Asus4/D  G#m7  B5/F# x2]
                          [4.F#m/A  B  E x2  B5]
```

Verse 2:
His enemies will run for sure,
The church will stand, she will endure.
He holds the keys of life, our Lord,
Death has no sting, no final word.

Taken from
SEE THE MORNING
Chris Tomlin
SURCD5084

HEAR YOUR PEOPLE SAYING YES

(Yes, and amen)

Matt Redman, Josiah Bell
& Robert Marvin

Em   G   D/F♯   A/C♯   C   Bm

Verse 1:
Em
   Hear Your people saying yes,
                             G
   Hear Your people saying yes to You.
Em
    Yes to anything You ask,
                       G
    Yes to anything we're called to do.

Verse 2:
Hear Your people say amen,
Hear Your people say amen to You.
Let Your kingdom come on earth,
Let it be just like we prayed to You.

Chorus:
           G
Yes and amen to everything that's in Your heart,
       D/F♯
Yes and amen to everything that You have planned.
    A/C♯
We live to see Your will be done,
   C   G   [1.3. Bm] [2.4.D/F♯] [End. Bm G]
And see Your perfect kingdom come on earth, on the earth.

1: To v.3, 2: & 4: Chorus 2, 3: To v.1.

Chorus 2:
           G
Yes and amen, we're taking up our cross for You.
        D/F♯
Give us the strength to take these dreams and follow through.
    A/C♯
We live to see Your will be done,
   C   G
And see Your perfect kingdom come on earth, on the earth.

Verse 3:
All the promises are yes,
All the promises are yes in You.
Every good and perfect gift,
Every blessing that we have was You.

Taken from
BEAUTIFUL NEWS
Matt Redman
SURCD5071

HERE I AM

(Blessing)

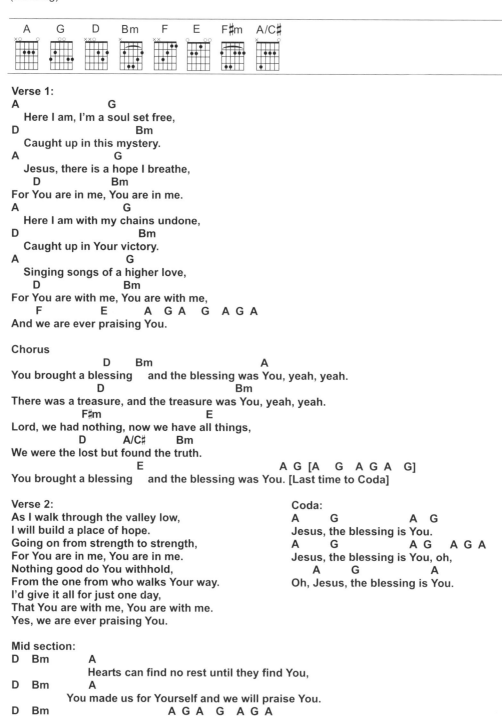

Verse 1:

A   G
  Here I am, I'm a soul set free,
D   Bm
  Caught up in this mystery.
A   G
  Jesus, there is a hope I breathe,
    D   Bm
For You are in me, You are in me.
A   G
  Here I am with my chains undone,
D   Bm
  Caught up in Your victory.
A   G
  Singing songs of a higher love,
    D   Bm
For You are with me, You are with me,
   F   E   A GA G AGA
And we are ever praising You.

Chorus

          D   Bm   A
You brought a blessing   and the blessing was You, yeah, yeah.
          D   Bm
There was a treasure, and the treasure was You, yeah, yeah.
       F#m   E
Lord, we had nothing, now we have all things,
        D   A/C#   Bm
We were the lost but found the truth.
            E   A G [A G AGA G]
You brought a blessing   and the blessing was You. [Last time to Coda]

Verse 2:
As I walk through the valley low,
I will build a place of hope.
Going on from strength to strength,
For You are in me, You are in me.
Nothing good do You withhold,
From the one from who walks Your way.
I'd give it all for just one day,
That You are with me, You are with me.
Yes, we are ever praising You.

Coda:
A   G   A G
Jesus, the blessing is You.
A   G   A G   AGA
Jesus, the blessing is You, oh,
       A   G   A
Oh, Jesus, the blessing is You.

Mid section:
D Bm   A
      Hearts can find no rest until they find You,
D Bm   A
    You made us for Yourself and we will praise You.
D Bm   AGA G AGA
     We will praise You. [To chorus]

Taken from
BEAUTIFUL NEWS
Matt Redman
SURCD5071

HERE I STAND

Salvation

Simon Brading

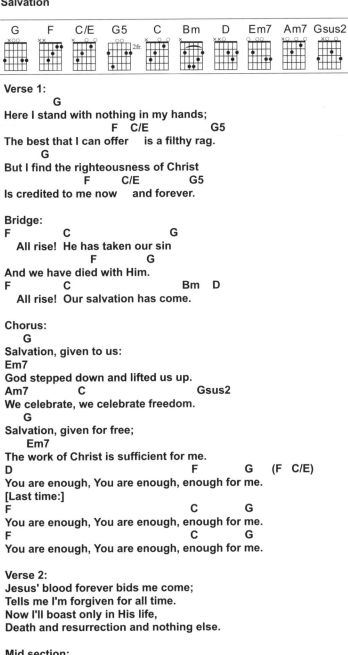

Verse 1:
       G
Here I stand with nothing in my hands;
                  F   C/E   G5
The best that I can offer   is a filthy rag.
     G
But I find the righteousness of Christ
                F   C/E   G5
Is credited to me now   and forever.

Bridge:
F   C   G
   All rise! He has taken our sin
                      F   G
And we have died with Him.
F   C   Bm   D
   All rise! Our salvation has come.

Chorus:
     G
Salvation, given to us:
Em7
God stepped down and lifted us up.
Am7   C   Gsus2
We celebrate, we celebrate freedom.
     G
Salvation, given for free;
       Em7
The work of Christ is sufficient for me.
D   F   G   (F C/E)
You are enough, You are enough, enough for me.
[Last time:]
F   C   G
You are enough, You are enough, enough for me.
F   C   G
You are enough, You are enough, enough for me.

Verse 2:
Jesus' blood forever bids me come;
Tells me I'm forgiven for all time.
Now I'll boast only in His life,
Death and resurrection and nothing else.

Mid section:
F   C   G
   All rise! He has taken our sin
And we have died with Him.
Dm   Am   G
   All rise! Our salvation has come.
F   C   G
   All rise! He has power over sin
And we are raised with HIm.
F   C   Bm   D
   All rise! Our salvation has come.

Taken from
LET THE RAIN COME
Newday Live
SURCD5109

HERE WE ARE

Remedy

David Crowder

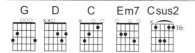

G   D   C   Em7 Csus2

Verse 1:
G   D C G   D C
Here we are, here we are,
    G   D   C
The broken amused, mistreated abused.
G   D C
Here we are.
    G   D C G   D C
Well, here You are, here You are,
    G   D   C
The beautiful One who came like a Son.
G   D C
Here You are.

Bridge 1:
       D   Em7
So we lift up our voices and open our hands
    Csus2
To cling to the love that we can't comprehend.
    D   Em7
Oh, lift up your voices and lift up your heads
    Csus2
To sing of the love that has freed us from sin.

Chorus:
         G   Csus2
He is the One who has saved us.
         G   Csus2
He is the One who embraced (2.&3. forgave) us.
         G   D   Csus2
He is the One who has come and is coming again.
         G   D Csus2 [1. G D Csus2 G D Csus2] [Last time: G]
He's the remedy.

Mid Section:
       D   Em7
Oh, I can't comprehend, I can't take it all in,
    Csus2
Never understand such perfect love,
              D
Come for the broken and beat,
        Em7
For the wounded and weak.
            Csus2
Oh, come, fall at His feet.
He's the remedy, He's the remedy.

Verse 2:
Here we are, here we are,
Bandaged and bruised, awaiting a cure. Here we are.
And here You are, here You are,
Our beautiful King, bringing relief. Here You are.

Bridge 2:
So we lift up our voices and open our hands,
Let go of the things that have kept us from Him.

Taken from
REMEDY
David Crowder Band
SURCD5101

HIGHER THAN THE STARS COULD BE

40.

Forever over us

Tré & Tori Sheppard, Mark Prentice, Paul Baker,
Jonny Ravn, Steve Evans & Nathan Dantzler

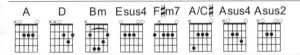

A D Bm Esus4 F#m7 A/C# Asus4 Asus2

Capo 4 (to play in original key of D♭)

Verse 1:
A
  Higher than the stars could be,
Further than the endless seas,
Far beyond tomorrow,
D
Your love carries me.
A
  I was lost, my heart asleep,
You gave everything for me.
When I called, You answered;
D
Your love rescued me.
Bm   Esus4
  You're everything I need.

Chorus:
A   F#m7
Jesus, forever over us
A/C#   D
You have written love.
A   F#m7
Saviour, You have rescued us;
    A/C#   D   [1.] A F#m7 A/C# D
Forever over us with love. [2. to ending] Asus4 A Asus2

Verse 2:
You're so much more than just belief -
King of all, but friend to me.
You have all of my heart,
You have captured me.
One day everyone will see,
Broken hearts will know Your peace;
There'll be no more sorrow -
We will all be free.

Mid section:
Bm   Esus4
  One day we will see.
   B   Esus4
And oh, we will be free!

Ending:
Asus4 A
Over us,
F#m7
Over us,
A/C#   D (A)
You have written love [Repeat]

Taken from
AS SURE AS THE STARS
Onehundredhours
SURCD5089

HOLY, HOLY GOD ALMIGHTY

(Holy)

Brenton Brown

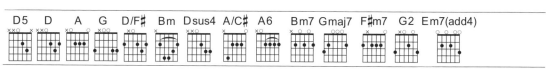

D5   D   A   G   D/F♯   Bm   Dsus4   A/C♯   A6   Bm7   Gmaj7   F♯m7   G2   Em7(add4)

Verse:
D5
Holy, Holy God Almighty,
Who was and is to come.
God of glory, You're so worthy,
All the saints bow down.

Chorus 1&2:
D   A   G   D
Holy is Your name in all the earth,
                      A   G   D
Righteous are Your ways so merciful,
        D/F♯   A   G   D
Everything You've done is just and true;
   D/F♯ G   A   D
Holy, holy God are You,
        G   A   D
Holy, holy God are You.

Mid section:
Bm   A   G   D
   All blessing,   all honour   belongs to You.
Bm   A   D Dsus4 D A/C♯
   All power,   all wisdom is Yours.
Bm   A   G   D
   All blessing,   all honour   belongs to You.
Bm   A   D Dsus4 D
   All power,   all wisdom is Yours.

Chorus 3:
            A6   Bm7   Gmaj7
Holy is Your name in all the earth,
                    A6   Gmaj7
Righteous are Your ways so merciful,
                    A6   Gmaj7
Everything You've done is just and true;
      G6   A6   Bm   [Play line 3x]
Holy, holy God are You,
      G6   A6
Holy, holy God are You.

End section:
| Bm | F♯m7 | G2 | G2 |
        Bm F♯m7   G2   Em7(add4)
Holy God, yeah.
            Bm   F♯m7   G2   Em7(add4)
Saints and angels bow in worship at Your feet, at Your feet.
            Bm   A/C♯   D
Saints and angels bow in worship, holy God.
D5
Holy, Holy God Almighty,
Who was and is to come.

Taken from
BECAUSE OF YOUR LOVE
Brenton Brown
SURCD5124

HOLY, HOLY IS THE LORD

Rain down

David Crowder

Bm Gmaj7 G D A

Capo 4(D)

Verse:
Ebm(Bm) Cbmaj7(Gmaj7)
Holy, holy is the Lord.
Ebm(Bm) Cbmaj7(Gmaj7) Ebm(Bm) Cbmaj7(Gmaj7)
Holy, holy is the Lord.
Ebm(Bm) Cbmaj7(Gmaj7)
Holy, holy is the Lord.
Ebm(Bm) Cbmaj7(Gmaj7)
Holy, holy is the Lord.

Chorus:
 Gb(D) Db(A)   Cb(G)
And rain   down Your love on us,
         Gb(D)
Rain down Your love.
    Db(A)   Cb(G)   Gb(D)
And rain   down Your grace and cover me.
 Db(A)   Cb(G)
Rain down Your love on us,
        Gb(D)
Rain down Your love.
   Db(A)   Cb(G) [1. Ebm(Bm) Cbmaj7(Gmaj7)] [Last time: Gb(D)]
And rain   down Your peace.

Taken from
REMEDY
David Crowder Band
SURCD5101

HOLY, UNCREATED ONE

(Uncreated One)

**Chris Tomlin
& J.D. Walt**

D   Em7   D/F♯   G   A   Asus4   A/C♯   Bm

Capo 1

Verse 1:
D Em7 D/F♯ G A   D
Holy   uncreated One,
       G   D/F♯ Asus4   A
Your beauty fills the skies.
             D   A/C♯   Bm   A
But the glory of Your majesty
           G   Asus4 A D
Is the mercy in   Your   eyes.

Verse 2:
Worthy, uncreated One,
From heaven to earth come down.
You laid aside Your royalty
To wear the sinner's crown.

Chorus:
     A   G   D
And O, great God, be glorified,
     A   G   D
Our lives laid down, Yours magnified.
     A   G A Bm
And O, great God, be lifted   high,
G   Asus4 A   D   Bm   Asus4 A   D   Bm   [1. Asus4 A]
There is none   like You.
[2.]
Asus4   A   D   Bm
There is none like You,
Asus4   A   D   Bm   Asus4 A [to end D]
There is none like You.

Verse 3:
Jesus, Saviour, God's own Son,
Risen, reigning Lord.
Sustainer of the universe
By the power of Your word.

Verse 4:
And when we see Your matchless face,
In speechless awe we'll stand.
And there we'll bow with grateful hearts,
Unto the Great I Am.

Taken from
SEE THE MORNING
Chris Tomlin
SURCD5084

HOLY, UNCREATED ONE

(Uncreated One)

43.

**Chris Tomlin
& J.E. Walt**

Capo 1

Verse 1:
Eb Fm7 Eb/G Ab Bb   Eb
Holy   uncreated One,
      Ab   Eb/G Bbsus4 Bb
Your beauty fills the skies.
       Eb   Bb/D Cm Bb
But the glory of Your majesty
     Ab   Bbsus4 Bb Eb
Is the mercy in   Your eyes.

Verse 2:
Worthy, uncreated One,
From heaven to earth come down.
You laid aside Your royalty
To wear the sinner's crown.

Chorus:
    Bb   Ab   Eb
And O, great God, be glorified,
    Bb   Ab   Eb
Our lives laid down, Yours magnified.
    Bb   Ab Bb Cm
And O, great God, be lifted high,
Ab   Bbsus4 Bb   Eb   Cm Bbsus4 Bb Eb Cm [1. Bbsus4 Bb]
There is none   like You.
[2.]
Bbsus4   Bb Eb   Cm
There is none like You,
Bbsus4   Bb Eb Cm Bbsus4 Bb [to end Eb]
There is none like You.

Verse 3:
Jesus, Saviour, God's own Son,
Risen, reigning Lord.
Sustainer of the universe
By the power of Your word.

Verse 4:
And when we see Your matchless face,
In speechless awe we'll stand.
And there we'll bow with grateful hearts,
Unto the Great I Am.

Taken from
SEE THE MORNING
Chris Tomlin
SURCD5084

HOW CAN I BECOME?

(Forgiven)

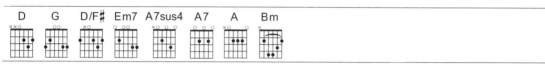

Verse 1:
```
       D                 G         D/F#
   How can I become    all that I can be?
Em7                A7sus4   A7           D
   How on earth can I         finally be free?
                         G
Though I'm far from home,
         D/F#   Em7
How can I return
                      A7sus4
Knowing that Your love
     A            D
Is nothing I can earn.
```

Chorus:
```
         G
Forgiven,
         D/F#   Em7
Forgiven,
         A7sus4
Forgiven,
     A      [D to end]
Forgiven.
```

Verse 2:
My heart is black and cold, so filthy with my sin.
I know it's only You that makes me new within.
You quiet me with Your love,
Now I can hear Your song.
You sing it over me
And now I know that I belong.

Mid section:
```
Bm   A   D
Oh,
                G
Clothed in majesty,
         D/F#      Em7
Yet mindful of me.
Bm   A   D
Oh,
                     G
You've come into my heart,
       D/F#   Em7       A
Saviour, redeemer, You've set me apart.
```

Taken from
BREATHE
Andy Smith
SURCD5073

HOW LONG?

Al Gordon

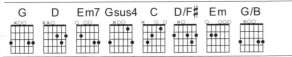

G   D   Em7 Gsus4   C   D/F#   Em   G/B

Capo 4

Verse 1:
   B(G)
How long till we gaze upon Your face,
F#(D)   B(G)
Gaze upon Your face, gaze upon Your face?
  G#m7(Em7) B(G)
Jesus, we will gaze upon Your face
F#(D)   B(G)
In the morning light.

Verse 2:
   G#m(Em)   B(G)
How long till You wipe these tears away,
F#(D)   B(G)
Wipe these tears away, wipe these tears away?
  G#m7(Em7) B(G)
Jesus, You will wipe these tears away,
F#(D)   B(G)
When the morning comes.

Verse 3:
   B(G)
How long till there's justice on the earth,
F#(D)   B(G)
Justice on the earth, justice on the earth?
  G#m7(Em7)   B(G)
Jesus, there'll be justice on the earth,
F#(D)   Bsus4(Gsus4) B(G)
When You come again.

Verse 4:
   G#m(Em)   B(G)
How long till we hear the victory roar,
F#(D)   B(G)
Hear the victory roar, hear the victory roar?
  G#m7(Em7) F#/A#(D/F#)   B(G)
Jesus, we   will   hear the victory roar,
F#(D)   B(G)
When this race is run.

Bridge:
   E(C)   B(G)   F#/A#(D/F#)
Yes, I know You will come.
   E(C)   B(G) F#/A#(D/F#)
Yes, I know You've already won.
   E(C)   G#m(Em) F#/A#(D/F#) E(C)
Yes, I know my Redeem - er   lives,
  G#m(Em) F#/A#(D/F#) Bsus4(Gsus4) B(G)   Bsus4(Gsus4) B(G)
My Redeem - er   lives.

Chorus:
E(C)   B/D#(G/B)
Come, Lord Jesus!
  G#m(Em)   F#/A#(D/F#)
We are desperate for You here!
  E(C)   B/D#(G/B)
Come, Lord Jesus!
  G#m(Em)   F#/A#(D/F#) [Last time:] E(C)
All creation calling out!

Ending:
   E(C)   B(G)   F#/A#(D/F#)
Yes, I know You will come.
   E(C)   B(G) F#/A#(D/F#)
Yes, I know You've already won.

Taken from
FUTURE SOUND
Al Gordon
SURCD5125

I AM CHOSEN
(Holding nothing back)

Tim Hughes
& Martin Smith

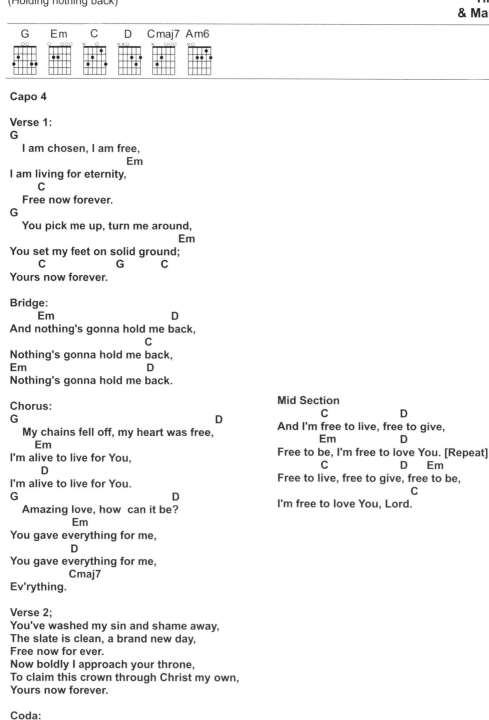

G   Em   C   D   Cmaj7 Am6

Capo 4

Verse 1:
G
  I am chosen, I am free,
                     Em
I am living for eternity,
     C
  Free now forever.
G
  You pick me up, turn me around,
                        Em
You set my feet on solid ground;
    C   G   C
Yours now forever.

Bridge:
     Em   D
And nothing's gonna hold me back,
                  C
Nothing's gonna hold me back,
Em   D
Nothing's gonna hold me back.

Chorus:
G   D
  My chains fell off, my heart was free,
  Em
I'm alive to live for You,
   D
I'm alive to live for You.
G   D
  Amazing love, how can it be?
      Em
You gave everything for me,
       D
You gave everything for me,
         Cmaj7
Ev'rything.

Verse 2;
You've washed my sin and shame away,
The slate is clean, a brand new day,
Free now for ever.
Now boldly I approach your throne,
To claim this crown through Christ my own,
Yours now forever.

Coda:
D   C
  I give everything for You,
       Em   Am6
I give everything for You, everything.

Mid Section
      C   D
And I'm free to live, free to give,
           Em   D
Free to be, I'm free to love You. [Repeat]
         C   D   Em
Free to live, free to give, free to be,
                      C
I'm free to love You, Lord.

Taken from
HOLDING NOTHING BACK
Tim Hughes
SURCD5068

I AM CHOSEN
(Holding nothing back)

Verse 1:
B
  I am chosen, I am free,
                     G#m
I am living for eternity,
     E
  Free now forever.
B
  You pick me up, turn me around,
                       G#m
You set my feet on solid ground;
   E   B   E
Yours now forever.

Bridge:
    G#m   F#
And nothing's gonna hold me back,
                     E
Nothing's gonna hold me back,
G#m   F#
Nothing's gonna hold me back.

Chorus:
B   F#
  My chains fell off, my heart was free,
   G#m
I'm alive to live for You,
    F#
I'm alive to live for You.
B   F#
  Amazing love, how can it be?
       G#m
You gave everything for me,
       F#
You gave everything for me,
        Emaj7
Ev'rything.

Verse 2;
You've washed my sin and shame away,
The slate is clean, a brand new day,
Free now for ever.
Now boldly I approach your throne,
To claim this crown through Christ my own,
Yours now forever.

Coda:
F#   E
  I give everything for You,
      G#m   C#m6
I give everything for You, everything.

Mid Section
       E   F#
And I'm free to live, free to give,
       G#m   F#
Free to be, I'm free to love You. [Repeat]
       E   F#   G#m
Free to live, free to give, free to be,
                   E
I'm free to love You, Lord.

Taken from
HOLDING NOTHING BACK
Tim Hughes
SURCD5068

I AM COMING ALIVE TO YOU

Coming alive

Paul Oakley

D   Em   G   Bm   D/F♯

Verse 1:
D
I am coming alive to You.
I could never deny
       Em
You are all that I want,
G   D
All that I need, Jesus.
D
You took all of my shame,
At the cross You made a way.
        Em
There is no greater love:
   G   D
You poured out Your life, Jesus.

Bridge:
      Bm   G   D
And if the stars fall from the sky,
      Bm   G   D
And if the sun should fail to shine,
       Bm   G   D/F♯
I know Your love will never die,
Em   G   D
I will be Yours forever more, Jesus.

Chorus:
D   Bm
   There is no-one else like You!
          G
No-one else so true:
       D
Jesus, only You
D   Bm
   Your love washed away my shame,
         G
Breaks away my chains,
        D
Makes my life brand new.

Verse 2:
There is no other name;
Yesterday, tomorrow, today -
You are always the same,
You never change, Jesus.
No eye ever has seen
And no mind could ever conceive
All the good that You have
Waiting in store for us.

Taken from
LET THE RAIN COME
Newday Live
SURCD5109

I AM NOT A STRANGER TO MERCY

(Take it to the streets)

Matt Redman
& Martin Smith

48.

G D/F♯ C/E Am7 C Em7 D

Capo 4

Verse 1:
```
G                                   D/F♯
I am not a stranger to mercy, for You found me,

Wrapped Your truth around me.
C/E
I am not a stranger to grace,
        Am7
I have seen it in Your face.
G
I am not a stranger to kindness,
            D/F♯
We're the broken with Your life inside us.
C/E
You have brought Your gospel to me,
        Am7
And I breathe it every day.
        C      Em7       D
How did I   become    Your miracle?
        C          Em7    D
Now to take    Your truth    and tell the world.
```

Chorus:
```
G
I'm going to take it to the streets,
D
I'm going to sing it 'til we meet.
C
Heaven is open,
        Am7
Come on all the earth rejoice.
G
I'm going to take it to the streets,
D
Wake up the dead heart from its sleep.
C
Heaven is open,                    [To end]
        Am7              1. [Em7]    2. [C   Am7   Em7]
Now's the time to raise our voice.      Oh.
```

Verse 2:
I must tell the world of this mercy, for You found me,
Wrapped Your truth around me.
I must tell the world of this grace,
I have seen it at Your cross.
I must tell the world of this kindness,
We're the broken with Your life inside us.
You have brought Your gospel to me,
Help me live it every day.
How did we become Your miracles?
Now to take Your truth and tell the world.

Taken from
BEAUTIFUL NEWS
Matt Redman
SURCD5071

I AM NOT A STRANGER TO MERCY

(Take it to the streets)

Matt Redman
& Martin Smith

Verse 1:
B   F#/A#
I am not a stranger to mercy, for You found me,

Wrapped Your truth around me.
E/G#
I am not a stranger to grace,
            C#m7
I have seen it in Your face.
B
I am not a stranger to kindness,
            F#/A#
We're the broken with Your life inside us.
E/G#
You have brought Your gospel to me,
            C#m7
And I breathe it every day.
         E   G#m7   F#
How did I   become   Your miracle?
         E   G#m7   F#
Now to take   Your truth   and tell the world.

Chorus:
B
I'm going to take it to the streets,
F#
I'm going to sing it 'til we meet.
E
Heaven is open,
        C#m7
Come on all the earth rejoice.
B
I'm going to take it to the streets,
F#
Wake up the dead heart from its sleep.
E
Heaven is open,   [To end]
        C#m7   1. [G#m7]   2. [E   C#m7   G#m]
Now's the time to raise our voice.   Oh.

Verse 2:
I must tell the world of this mercy, for You found me,
Wrapped Your truth around me.
I must tell the world of this grace,
I have seen it at Your cross.
I must tell the world of this kindness,
We're the broken with Your life inside us.
You have brought Your gospel to me,
Help me live it every day.
How did we become Your miracles?
Now to take Your truth and tell the world.

Taken from
BEAUTIFUL NEWS
Matt Redman
SURCD5071

Out of the darkness

Tim & Rachel Hughes

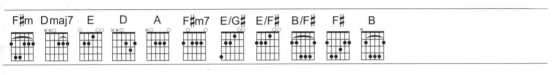

F#m   Dmaj7   E   D   A   F#m7   E/G#   E/F#   B/F#   F#   B

Verse 1:
F#m
   I could live a thousand years,
Dmaj7
   Never earn a moment of Your grace.
F#m
   Even in my darkest day,
  Dmaj7   E
You shine on me, You shine on me.

Chorus 1 & 2:
   D   A   E
And out of the darkness
          D   A   E
You brought me into Your glorious light.
        D   A   E
Saved from the death I was facing,
        D   A   E
Rejoicing in the future, a hope that is mine.

Verse 2:
The greatest of all gifts,
From the greatest of all givers.
Jesus, there upon the cross,
True love displayed for all to see.

Mid section:
      D   E
And Your grace runs after me,
     F#m   E/G#
Runs after me every day of my life.
      D   E
And Your mercies, they never fail,
     F#m   G   F#
They never fail, every day of my life.

Chorus 3:
   E/F#   B/F#   F#
And out of the darkness
         E/F#   B/F#   F#
You brought me into Your glorious light.
          E   B   F#
Saved from the death I was facing,
        E   B   F#
Rejoicing in the future, a hope that is mine.
   E   B   F#
And out of the darkness
         E   B   F#
You brought me into Your glorious light.
        E   B   F#
Saved from the death I was facing,
        E   B   F#
Rejoicing in the future, a hope that is mine.

Ending:
D   A   E
Out of the darkness,
D   A   E
Out of the darkness.

Taken from
HOLDING NOTHING BACK
Tim Hughes
SURCD5068

I DON'T KNOW HOW TO BREATHE

(There is always a song)

Paul Baloche, Steven Curtis-Chapman, Stuart Garrard, Israel Houghton
Tim Hughes, Graham Kendrick, Andy Park, Matt Redman
Martin Smith, Michael W. Smith, Chris Tomlin, Darlene Zschech

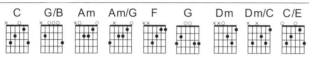

C   G/B   Am   Am/G   F   G   Dm   Dm/C   C/E

Verse 1:
```
C                              G/B
   I don't know how to breathe,
Am            Am/G       F
   I don't know how to leave you
C                              G/B
   I don't know what to say;
     Am          Am/G        F
And who am I to say it anyway?
```

Chorus:
```
            F
But there is always a song,
   G Am              G/B        C   G
And I try to sing along, over You.
C         F
   I can hear it being sung,
   G    Am            G/B       C   G   C
All of heaven sings along, over You.
```

[Not 1st time]
```
        F
There is always a song,
   G Am              G/B          C  [G   C]
And I'll try to sing along,   over You. [Last time x2]
```

Mid section:
```
Dm   Dm/C                  G/B
Sing, sing like You've never sung,
C           C/E   F
Sing for your joy to come.
Dm   Dm/C                  G/B
Sing, sing like You've  never sung,
C           C/E   F
Sing for your joy to come
```

Taken from
COMPASSIONART

IF YOU KNOW YOU'RE LOVED

D   D/C♯ D/F♯ Gmaj7

D
   If you know you're loved by the King,
    D/C♯
Sing, sing, sing.
D/F♯
   If you know you're loved by the King,
    Gmaj7
Live for Him, live for Him (oh).

[Last time]
    Gmaj7
Live for Him, live for Him, live for Him, live for Him.

Taken from
BEAUTIFUL NEWS
Matt Redman
SURCD5071

I KNOW LIFE IS A FRAGILE THING

52.

Mercy day

Tré & Tori Sheppard, Mark Prentice,
Paul Baker, Jonny Ravn & Steve Evans

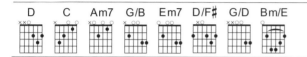

Verse 1:
D   C
 I know life is a fragile thing
D   Am7
 And knowing love is its greatest prize.
D   C
 But if our hearts carry so much pain
D   C
 How can there be room for love inside?

Chorus:
G/B C   D Em7
 Don't you need a mercy day,
G/B   C   D Em7
 Where everything gets cleared away
  D/F♯   G   D Em7
And grace falls down, our debts are paid.
G/B C   D Em7
 This could be your mercy day.

Verse 2:
If you find hope, can you make it stay?
If you find love, does it have to go away?
Don't you think it's time to find a better way?
Love is here: this is mercy day.

Mid section:
G/D G/B Bm/E   G/D G/B Bm/E
 There's a price you cannot pay.
G/D G/B Bm/E   G/D G/B Bm/E
 There's a price you cannot pay.
G/D G/B Bm/E   G/D G/B Bm/E
 There's a price you cannot pay.
G/D G/B Bm/E   G/D G/B Bm/E
 There's a price you cannot pay.

Last chorus:
Don't you need a mercy day,
Where everything gets cleared away
And grace falls down, our debts are paid.
Come on in, it' s mercy day.

Ending:
G/B C D Em7
Grace falls down,
G/B C D Em7
Debts are paid.
G/B C D Em7
Grace falls down,
G/B C D Em7 (N.C. note=E)
Debts are paid.

Taken from
AS SURE AS THE STARS
Onehundredhours
SURCD5089

I KNOW THERE ARE MILLIONS JUST LIKE ME   53.

Hold on

Tré & Tori Sheppard
& Kathryn Scott

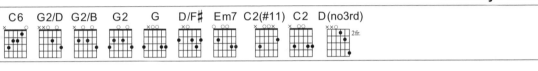

C6   G2/D   G2/B   G2   G   D/F♯   Em7   C2(♯11)   C2   D(no3rd)

Verse 1:

             C6
I know there are millions just like me,
       G2/D   G2/B
I know how it looks on your T.V.
       C6   G
If you only knew the way my sister's eyes can smile.
           C6
I wish you could walk with me today
        G2/D   G2/B
And hold my hand, talking all the way.
        C6   G2
I'd show you my life, my hope, my chances slipping by.

Chorus:

   G   D/F♯
So, hold on, don't lose me
              Em7
Though I'm just one face
       C2(♯11)   C2
In a cast of thousands.
G   D/F♯
   Hold on, can't you see
        Em7
Hope is dying all around us,
         C2(♯11)
The water is rising and I'm drowning.
G
   You gotta hold on,
D(no 3rd)   G
   You gotta hold on to me.

Verse 2:

Will you remember me this way
Or will my picture slowly fade
As sure as the stars around are falling one by one?
'Cause I'm getting closer to the edge
Of yesterday's broken promises
And 'happily ever after' never, never comes.

Mid section:

   G   D/F♯
   You gotta hold on,   please.
Em7   C2(♯11)
   You gotta hold on.
   G   D/F♯
   You gotta hold on,   please.
Em7   C2(♯11)
   You gotta hold on.

Taken from
AS SURE AS THE STARS
Onehundredhours
SURCD5089

IN A DYING, HURTING WORLD

You're the light

Ben Cantelon

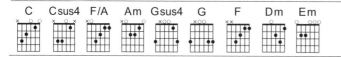

C   Csus4   F/A   Am   Gsus4   G   F   Dm   Em

Verse:
C   Csus4   C
  In a dying, hurting world
        Csus4   F/A   Am   F/A   Am
There's a light that shines for all to see.
C   Csus4   C
  Though the sky may turn to grey
       Csus4   F/A   Am   F/A   Am
And broken hearts begin to fade away,
Am   Gsus4
  Your love shines through,
G   Gsus4   G   F   Dm
  Daylight breaks through the longest of nights.

Chorus:
F
You're the light that shines,
C   G
Shining bright for all the world to see,
          Dm
Yes, the world will see.
      F
You're radiant in all Your glory;
C   G
Nothing is impossible for You,
         Dm   [2.] F   [Last time:] F   C
Impossible for You.

Verse 2:
God of mercy, God of grace,
Let justice flow like we have never known.
Give us courage, give us faith,
Faith for miracles we've longed to see.
The deaf will hear You.
The blind will see You.
Let the dead man arise!

Mid section:
      F   Em
Would You shine?
      Am   G
Would You shine?
      F   Em
Would You shine?
      Am   G
Would You shine?

Taken from
DAYLIGHT BREAKS THROUGH
Ben Cantelon
SURCD5094
and
LIVING FOR YOUR GLORY
Soul Survivor Live 2007
SURCD5108

IN ALL GLORY
(My God reigns)

Martin Cooper

G   C   Em   Am   D

Capo 2:

Verse 1:
```
G                 C
  In all glory,     the Almighty:
Em                      C
  Hallelujah, my God reigns.
G                 C
  You are worthy,    One so holy:
Em                      C
  Hallelujah, my God reigns.
Am                      G
I will bow, bow to You alone;
Am          C              D
King of kings, seated on Your throne.
```

Chorus:
```
                G
My God reigns,
                    D
Highest praise belongs to You.
                Em
My God reigns,
            D
Ever faithful, always good.
                G
My God reigns,
                    D
Kingdoms rise and kingdoms fall.
                Am              D
But You reign over all, forevermore
                [1. G    C]
My God reigns.[2. Em  D   C x2]
                [3. G    D   Am  D   G]
```

Verse 2:
King of glory, You have found me:
Hallelujah, my God reigns.
In your presence, I am changing:
Hallelujah, my God reigns.
I will trust, trust in You laone.
You're the Rock, You are my great hope.

IN ALL GLORY

(My God reigns)

Martin Cooper

A   D   F♯m   Bm   E

Verse 1:
A   D
  In all glory,   the Almighty:
F♯m   D
  Hallelujah, my God reigns.
A   D
  You are worthy,   One so holy:
F♯m   D
  Hallelujah, my God reigns.
Bm   A
I will bow, bow to You alone;
Bm   D   E
King of kings, seated on Your throne.

Chorus:
                         A
My God reigns,
                              E
Highest praise belongs to You.
                    F♯m
My God reigns,
                E
Ever faithful, always good.
                    A
My God reigns,
                         E
Kingdoms rise and kingdoms fall.
                    Bm   E
But You reign over all, forevermore
                    [1. A   D]
My God reigns.[2. F♯m E   D x2]
                    [3. A   E   Bm   E   A]

Verse 2:
King of glory, You have found me:
Hallelujah, my God reigns.
In your presence, I am changing:
Hallelujah, my God reigns.
I will trust, trust in You laone.
You're the Rock, You are my great hope.

IN THE BEGINNING

(Centre of it all)

G2 Asus2 D2/F♯   D   G   A   D/F♯ Asus4 Aadd4 Dadd4/F♯

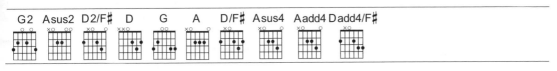

Capo 2

Verse 1:
G2
   In the beginning,
      Asus2   D2/F♯   G2
Before You set the world in motion,
            Asus2   D2/F♯
Uncreated, God eternal.

G2
   Radiant beauty,
   Asus2   D2/F♯   G2
Infinite, the Godhead, Three in One,
          Asus2   D2/F♯
Perfect Father, Spirit, Saviour.

Chorus:
       G
And it all begins and ends with You,
  A   D/F♯
It all begins and ends with You,
    G   Asus4   Dsus2 [G2]
The First and Last, the centre of it all.
         G
And in You all things are held together,
  A   D/F♯
Sun, the moon, the stars, the heavens,
    G   G2 G Aadd4 Dadd4/F♯
Creator God, the centre of it all.

Verse 2:
All of the universe explodes in song
Before Designer King,
Valley shaper, Mountain Maker.
The stars sing out, they can't contain
Their praises of their God,
Earth Creator, Heaven Shaker.

G2
   Beginning of it all
A2   D/F♯   G2
   The reason for it all,
                [1. A2   D/F♯]
The centre of it all [x2]

Taken from
HOLDING NOTHING BACK
Tim Hughes
SURCD5068

IN THE BEGINNING

(Centre of it all)

Verse 1:
A2
   In the beginning,
       Bsus2   E2/G♯   A2
Before You set the world in motion,
            Bsus2   E2/G♯
Uncreated, God eternal.

A2
   Radiant beauty,
   Bsus2   E2/G♯   A2
Infinite, the Godhead, Three in One,
             Bsus2   E2/G♯
Perfect Father, Spirit, Saviour.

Chorus:
       A
And it all begins and ends with You,
 B   E/G♯
It all begins and ends with You,
       A   Bsus4   Esus2 [A2]
The First and Last, the centre of it all.
         A
And in You all things are held together,
   B   E/G♯
Sun, the moon, the stars, the heavens,
       A   A2 A Badd4 Eadd4/G♯
Creator God, the centre of it all.

Verse 2:
All of the universe explodes in song
Before Designer King,
Valley shaper, Mountain Maker.
The stars sing out, they can't contain
Their praises of their God,
Earth Creator, Heaven Shaker.

A2
   Beginning of it all
B2   E/G♯   A2
   The reason for it all,
              [1. B2   E/G♯]
The centre of it all [x2]

Taken from
HOLDING NOTHING BACK
Tim Hughes
SURCD5068

IN THE NAME OF THE FATHER

Our God saves

Paul Baloche & Brenton Brown

Verse:
          D
In the name of the Father, in the name of the Son,
           Gsus2
In the name of the Spirit, Lord, we come.
          Bm7
We're gathered together to lift up Your name,
     Gsus2
To call on our Saviour, to fall on Your grace.

Bridge:
    D
Hear the joyful sound of our offering
    A
As Your saints bow down, as Your people sing.
       Bm7
We will rise with You, lifted on Your wings,
    G2
And the world will see that

Chorus 1:
      D   A
Our God saves, our God saves,
    Bm7   G2 | D | D | Gsus2 | Gsus2 |
There is hope, in Your name. Yeah, yeah.

Chorus 2:
      D   A
Our God saves, our God saves,
    Bm7   G2
There is hope, in Your name.
        D   A
Mourning turns to songs of praise;
        Bm7   G2
Our God saves, our God saves

Instrumental section:
| D | D | A | A | Bm7 | Bm7 | Gsus2 | Gsus2 |

Ending:
D
    Our God saves, our God saves.

Taken from
BECAUSE OF YOUR LOVE
Brenton Brown
SURCD5124

I SEE THE KING OF GLORY

Hosanna

C Am Dm G C/E Fsus2 Gsus4 Am7 Dmsus2 Em F2

Capo 4(C)

Verse 1:
E(C)
   I see the King of glory
C♯m(Am)
Coming on the clouds with fire.
              F♯m(Dm)
The whole earth shakes,
              B(G)
The whole earth shakes.
E(C)
   I see His love and mercy
C♯m(Am)
Washing over all our sin.
         F♯m(Dm)
The people sing,
         B(G)
The people sing.

Chorus:
   E/G♯(C/E) Asus2(Fsus2)   Bsus4(Gsus4) C♯m7(Am7)
Hosan - na,   hosan - na,
  Asus2(Fsus2) C♯m(Am)   B(G)
Hosanna in the highest.
   E/G♯(C/E) Asus2(Fsus2)   Bsus4(Gsus4) C♯m7(Am7)
Hosan - na,   hosan - na,
  Asus2(Fsus2) B(G)   C♯m(Am)
Hosanna in the highest.

Verse 2:
I see a generation
Rising up to take their place
With selfless faith, with selfless faith.
I see a new revival,
Stirring as we pray and seek.
We're on our knees, we're on our knees.

Mid section:
| C♯m(Am) | Esus2(Csus2) | F♯msus2(Dmsus2) | G♯m (Em) |
| C♯m(Am) | Esus2(Csus2) | F♯msus2(Dmsus2) | G♯m (Em) |
A2(F2)   Bsus4(Gsus4)
Heal my heart and make it clean;
E(C)   C♯m(Am)
Open up my eyes to the things unseen.
A2(F2)   Bsus4(Gsus4)   C♯m(Am)   C♯m7(Am7)
Show me how to love like You have loved me.
A2(F2)   Bsus4(Gsus4)
Break my heart for what breaks Yours.
E(C)   C♯m(Am)
Everything I am's for Your kingdom's cause,
A2(F2)   Bsus4(Gsus4)   A2(F2)
As I walk from earth into eternity.

Ending:
  Asus2(Fsus2) B(G)   C♯m(Am)
Hosanna in the highest.
  Asus2(Fsus2) B(G)   C♯m(Am)
Hosanna in the highest.
  Asus2(Fsus2) B(G)   E(C)
Hosanna in the highest.

Taken from
GOD OF THIS CITY
Passion
SURCD5126

I STAND AMAZED

(How marvellous)

G   D   C   D/F♯ Em7 Am

Capo 1

Verse 1:
```
 G
I stand amazed in the presence
    D          C    G
Of Jesus the Nazarene,
         C               G
And wonder how He could love me,
             D      G
A sinner condemned, unclean.
```

Chorus:
```
C
Singing:
G
How marvellous, how wonderful,
D
And my song shall ever be.
G        D/F# Em7
How marvellous, how wonderful
Am   Em7    D      G   [1.C Repeat v.1] [2. C   Em7   G]
Is my Saviour's love for me.
```

Verse 2:
For me it was in the garden He prayed,
'Not my will, but thine'
He had no tears for His own griefs,
But sweat drops of blood for mine.

Verse 3:
He took my sins and my sorrows,
He made them His very own;
He bore the burden to Calv'ry,
And suffered and died alone.

Verse 4:
And with the ransomed in glory,
His face I at last shall see,
It will be my joy through the ages,
To sing of His love for me.

Taken from
PASSION
Everything Glorious
SURCD5079

I STAND AMAZED

(How marvellous)

Verse 1:
  A♭
I stand amazed in the presence
    E♭   D♭   A♭
Of Jesus the Nazarene,
      D♭   A♭
And wonder how He could love me,
             E♭   A♭
A sinner condemned, unclean.

Chorus:
D♭
Singing:
A♭
How marvellous, how wonderful,
E♭
And my song shall ever be.
A♭   E♭/G Fm7
How marvellous, how wonderful
Cm   Fm7   E♭   A♭   [1.D♭ Repeat v.1] [2. D♭   Fm7 A♭]
Is my Saviour's love for me.

Verse 2:
For me it was in the garden He prayed,
'Not my will, but thine'
He had no tears for His own griefs,
But sweat drops of blood for mine.

Verse 3:
He took my sins and my sorrows,
He made them His very own;
He bore the burden to Calv'ry,
And suffered and died alone.

Verse 4:
And with the ransomed in glory,
His face I at last shall see,
It will be my joy through the ages,
To sing of His love for me.

Taken from
PASSION
Everything Glorious
SURCD5079

IT'S JUST IMPOSSIBLE TO FIND THE WORDS 60.

Paul Oakley

My wonder

A C#m E/B B E/G# F#m

Verse 1:

A   C#m   E/B
It's just impossible to find the words - You're just so amazing.

A   C#m   E/B
And when I think of what You've done for me - well, I can't contain it.

A   C#m   E/B
You give me riches that I don't deserve - and I can't repay it.

A   C#m
But if the universe was mine to give,
       B   B B A A E/G# A B
Well I'd give it all, but You made it anyway.

Chorus:

E   B   F#m   A
You are my Wonder, there's no other love that I could live for.

E   B   F#m   A   B
And I will never be the same again: You've got my heart.

E   B   F#m   A
And all the joy You bring is more than I could ever dream of.

E   B   A A A A F#m F#m B
No one could ever take Your place.

[1st time:]

A   E/G#
You alone could be the fire in my heart,

A   B B A A E/G# A B
So fan the spark into a flame,
          B B A A E/G# A B
For Your name.

[2nd time]

A   E/G#
You alone can turn my life inside out,

A   B
To the wonder of Your name.

A   E/G#
You alone could be the fire in my heart,

A   B B A A E/G# A B
So fan the spark into a flame,
          B B A A E/G# A B
For Your name,
        B B A A E/G# A B
Everyday.

[3rd time:]

A   E/G#
You alone could be the fire in my heart,

A   B B A A E/G# A B
So fan the spark into a flame,
          B B A A E/G# A B
Everyday,
        B B A A E/G# A B B A E/G# A B E
For Your name.

Taken from
LET THE RAIN COME
Newday Live
SURCD5109

IT'S YOUR BLOOD THAT SAVED ME

(To You be the glory)

61.

Sim Walker
& Chris Sayburn

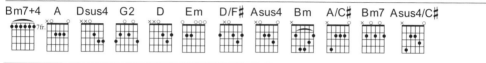

Bm7+4   A   Dsus4   G2   D   Em   D/F♯   Asus4   Bm   A/C♯   Bm7   Asus4/C♯

Capo 1

Verse 1:
Bm7+4   A   Dsus4
  It's Your blood that saved me,
Bm7+4   A   G2
  It's Your blood that never fails.
Bm7+4 A   D   Em   D/F♯   G
  Your sacrifice for all, made perfect on the cross,
       D/F♯ Em Asus4   G
You opened up the way to eternal life.

Chorus:
Bm   Asus4   D
  To You be the glory,
Bm   Asus4   Em
  To You be the praise;
Bm   A/C♯   F♯m7
  As we crown You with glory, we declare:
   G   A   D
1.3.5. God of heaven, You reign.
   G   A   Bm   A/C♯
2.   God of heaven, You reign. To You be the . . .
   G   A   D   A/C♯ Bm
4.   God of heaven, You reign.   To You be the . . .

Verse 2:
You alone are worthy,
You deserve our highest praise.
In awe we stand amazed,
That You would take our place;
You opened up the way
Into eternal life.

Mid section:
  Asus4   Bm7   G   Asus4
Forever, forever, forever You shall reign.
       Bm7   G   Asus4
Forever, forever, forever You shall reign.
  Asus4/C♯ Bm7   G   Asus4
Forever, forever, forever You shall reign.
  Asus4/C♯ Bm7   G   Asus4
Forever, forever, forever You shall reign.

Taken from
THE PEOPLE'S ALBUM, 3,
SURCD5140

I WILL CHOOSE TO PRAISE YOU

62.

(Choose a hallelujah)

Cathy Burton
& David Gate

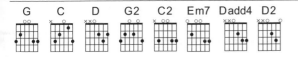

G   C   D   G2   C2   Em7   Dadd4   D2

Verse 1:
G
I will choose to praise You
    C
With everything that's in me.
  D   C
I'm laying down my pride filled heart
                      G2
So it won't hold me back.

Verse 2:
I give You all that I am,
My life I place in Your hands.
For Your worship I was made
To give my life in praise with You.

Chorus:
    C2
So I choose the song of heaven,
              Em7
And I choose a 'halelujah';
        Dadd4
For You are high above anything
    C2   G2
That turns my love from You. [1st time to v.3]
      C2
And with every road before me,
   Em7
I will choose the path that's costly;

For You are high above anything
   C2   [1. G2] [2. G]
That turns my love from You.

Verse 3:
I am your creation,
Made to give You glory.
So I'm finding every way i can
To serve You, Lord.

Mid section:
D   Em7   C
   Give me a heart that is only devoted to You:
D   Em7   C
   Undivided and faithful to all that is true,
D   Em7   C   D
   Determined to see Your kingdom break through, breakthrough.

Coda:
G   C2   Em7
  Oh,   oh,
        D2   C2   G
You are high above anything that turns my love from You.

JESUS CHRIST, YOU NEVER CHANGE

Morning Star

Al Gordon & Tim Hughes

Verse 1:
A   Bm
Jesus Christ, You never change,
A/C♯   D
Yesterday, today the same.
A   Bm
Morning Star, the rising sun,
     A/C♯   D
With You the best is yet to come.
E   F♯m
   Christ has died,   Christ is risen
D   E
Christ will come again.

Chorus:
A   E
King for evermore.
             F♯m   D
It's You I'm living for, it's You I'm living for.
A   E
Brightest Morning Star,
           Bm   D   [1.] A   Bm   F♯m   D
How beautiful You are, how beautiful You are.

Verse 2:
Can you hear the future sound
That rises up to shake the ground?
All around the world we sing
The anthem of the coming King.
God who was, God who is,
God who is to come.

Mid section:
     E   F♯m7   D
I am Yours, Jesus, Yours.
     E   F♯m7   D
I am Yours, always Yours

Ending:
A   Bm
Can you hear the future sound
A/C♯   D
Rising up all around
    A   Bm   A/C♯   D
How beautiful You are.
    A   Bm
We see the star that's breaking through,
  A/C♯   D
Eternity is all for You.
     A   Bm   A/C♯   D
How beautiful You are.
A   Bm   A/C♯   D   A
   Beautiful You are.

Taken from
FUTURE SOUND
Al Gordon
SURCD5125

JESUS, YOU ARE HERE WITH US
64.

(Won't stay silent)

Paul Baloche, Steven Curtis-Chapman, Stuart Garrard, Israel Houghton,
Tim Hughes, Graham Kendrick, Andy Park, Matt Redman,
Martin Smith, Michael W. Smith, Chris Tomlin, Darlene Zschech

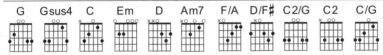

G   Gsus4   C   Em   D   Am7   F/A   D/F♯   C2/G   C2   C/G

Capo 3:

Verse 1:
G   Gsus4
Jesus, You are here with us,
     G   Gsus4
Our hearts are being stirred.
C
Spirit, intercede for us,
                          G
With groans too deep for words.

Bridge:
Em   D
Teach us how to pray;
Am7   C
Could we be a prayerful people?
Em   D
Shake us up today, Lord.

Chorus:
              G   D
We're coming out, on our knees,
          F/A   C
Desprate, Lord, for You to be
     G   D
In our cities, in our streets,
          F/A   C
Lifted high for all to see.
              Em   D/F♯   G
We won't stay silent anymore,
              Em   D/F♯   [C2/G]
We won't stay silent anymore. [Last time C2]

Verse 2:
Holy Father, hear our cry,
We're knocking on Your door,
Help us Lord to persevere,
You know we long for more.

Mid section:
G   D   F   C
  Oh,   won't stay silent, won't stay silent. [Repeat x3]
Em D/F♯ C/G   C
  Oh,   won't stay silent.   We're coming out . . .

Taken from
COMPASSIONART

JESUS, YOU ARE HERE WITH US

(Won't stay silent)

Paul Baloche, Steven Curtis-Chapman, Stuart Garrard, Israel Houghton,
Tim Hughes, Graham Kendrick, Andy Park, Matt Redman,
Martin Smith, Michael W. Smith, Chris Tomlin, Darlene Zschech

Verse 1:
B♭   B♭sus4
Jesus, You are here with us,
  B♭   B♭sus4
Our hearts are being stirred.
E♭
Spirit, intercede for us,
       B♭
With groans too deep for words.

Bridge:
Gm   F
Teach us how to pray;
Cm7 E♭
Could we be a prayerful people?
Gm   F
Shake us up today, Lord.

Chorus:
     B♭   F
We're coming out, on our knees,
   A♭/C   E♭
Desprate, Lord, for You to be
  B♭   F
In our cities, in our streets,
  A♭/C   E♭
Lifted high for all to see.
    Gm F/A B♭
We won't stay silent anymore,
    EGm F/A [E♭2/B♭]
We won't stay silent anymore. [Last time E♭2]

Verse 2:
Holy Father, hear our cry,
We're knocking on Your door,
Help us Lord to persevere,
You know we long for more.

Mid section:
B♭ F A♭   E♭
 Oh, won't stay silent, won't stay silent. [Repeat x3]
Gm F/A E♭/B♭   E♭
 Oh, won't stay silent. We're coming out . . .

Taken from
COMPASSIONART

JOY IS THE THEME
(Beautiful news)

Matt Redman

A   F   G   E   D   E/A

Verse:
A
Joy is the theme of my song,

And the beat of my heart,
                     F   G
And that joy is found   in You.
      A
For You showed the power of Your cross,

And Your great saving love,
                     F   G
And my soul woke up   to You.
E   D
   I heard Your beautiful news,
E   D
   Grace so amazing, so true.

Chorus:
A   E/A
   Shout it out, let the people sing,
   F   G
Something so powerful should shake the whole wide world.
A   E/A
   Make it loud, make it louder still,
 F   G   A [/   /   F G]
Saviour, we're singing now to celebrate Your beautiful news.

                                  [Last time]
                        F   G   A
                          . . . beautiful news.

Mid section:
Dm   C   A
   There's a God who came down to save,
Dm   C   A
   Showed the world His amazing grace.
Dm   C
   There's a God who came down to save,
      F   D6   D7
And He calls your name.
   A
   Shout it out . . . .

Taken from
BEAUTIFUL NEWS
Matt Redman
SURCD5071

KING OF ALL

Andy Smith

Am7 C/E F G Dm Em C

Capo 4

Verse 1:
```
Am7                        C/E
   King of all and yet You came,
                 Am7            C/E
You gave it all away,    gave it all away.
  Am7                     C/E
You chose the cross, You took my blame
                  Am7              C/E
And gave Yourself away,    gave Yourself away.
```

Bridge:
```
F                              G
  So this is how I know it's true:
                            F
It's not about me, it's about You.
                            G
I'm faceless, hidden in Your love,
                        Am7
A nameless warrior I'll become.
```

Chorus:
```
Am7
Jesus, You are awesome.
G               F        Am7
  You bridged the gap for me and
                    G  Dm
What You've done will last forever.
Am7
  You took the hope of glory
G             F
  And set it deep inside me;
F            G              Am7   [G  F  G  Am7]
  You reign supreme over all the earth.
```

Verse 2:
You made a call on me today
To give it all away, give it all away.
A promise I have made today,
Not just the words I say,
I'll give it all away.

Mid section:
```
Am7                        G    F
  You made a call on me today to give it all away.
  G                              Am7
  You made a call on me today to give it all away.
```

Taken from
BREATHE
Andy Smith
SURCD5073

KING OF ALL

Andy Smith

Verse 1:
```
C#m7                  E/G#
   King of all and yet You came,
                 C#m7            E/G#
You gave it all away,     gave it all away.
  C#m7                     E/G#
You chose the cross, You took my blame
                       C#m7          E/G#
And gave Yourself away,      gave Yourself away.
```

Bridge:
```
A                        B
   So this is how I know it's true:
                              A
It's not about me, it's about You.
                              B
I'm faceless, hidden in Your love,
                              C#m7
A nameless warrior I'll become.
```

Chorus:
```
C#m7
Jesus, You are awesome.
B              A          C#m7
   You bridged the gap for me and
                        B   F#m
What You've done will last forever.
C#m7
   You took the hope of glory
B            A
   And set it deep inside me;
A            B                   C#m7 [B  A  B  C#m7 ]
   You reign supreme over all the earth.
```

Verse 2:
You made a call on me today
To give it all away, give it all away.
A promise I have made today,
Not just the words I say,
I'll give it all away.

Mid section:
```
C#m7                   B    A
   You made a call on me today to give it all away.
B                        C#m7
   You made a call on me today to give it all away.
```

Taken from
BREATHE
Andy Smith
SURCD5073

KING OF GLORY

(Glorious)

Al Gordo

Bm Gsus2 D(no3rd) Dmaj7(no3rd)   Asus4   A   D

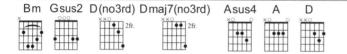

Intro: Bm Gsus2 D(no3rd) Dmaj7(no3rd) Bm Gsus2 D(no3rd) Asus4 A

Verse 1:
    D(no3rd)
The King of glory, King of light
 Gsus2   Bm A
I see You, I see You.
  D(no3rd)
Shining in the face of Christ
 Gsus2   Bm A
Your beauty Illuminates.
     Gsus2   A   D   Asus4 A
With brilliance brighter than the sun.

Chorus:
    Bm   Gsus2
And You are the one I love,
     D(no3rd) Dmaj7(no3rd)/C♯
You're glorious, glorious.
    Bm   Gsus2
And You have won my heart,
     D(no3rd) Dmaj7(no3rd)/C♯
You're glorious, glorious.

Verse 2:
Face to face, my life unveiled,
I worship, I worship You.
You're my everlasting light,
Your glory captivates.
With brilliance brighter than the sun.

Chorus x 2

Mid section:
   Gsus2 Bm   D(no3rd) Dmaj7(no3rd)/C♯
And I   won't turn my eyes   away,

   Gsus2 Bm   D(no3rd) Dmaj7(no3rd)/C♯
No, I   won't turn my eyes   away. [Repeat]

KING OF GLORY

(Glorious)

Al Gordon

Intro: C#m Asus2 E(no3rd)   Bsus4   C#m Asus2 E(no3rd) Bsus4 B

Verse 1:
    E(no3rd)
The King of glory, King of light
 Asus2   C#m B
I see You, I see You.
 E(no3rd)
Shining in the face of Christ
 Asus2   C#m B
Your beauty Illuminates.
    Asus2   B   E   Bsus4 B
With brilliance brighter than the sun.

Chorus:
    C#m   Asus2
And You are the one I love,
     E(no3rd) Bsus4
You're glorious, glorious.
    C#m   Asus2
And You have won my heart,
     E(no3rd) Bsus4
You're glorious, glorious.

Verse 2:
Face to face, my life unveiled,
I worship, I worship You.
You're my everlasting light,
Your glory captivates.
With brilliance brighter than the sun.

Chorus x 2

Mid section:
    Asus2 C#m   E(no3rd) Bsus4
And I   won't turn my eyes   away,

    Asus2 C#m   E(no3rd) Bsus4
No, I   won't turn my eyes   away. [Repeat]

LEAD ME

Brenton Brown

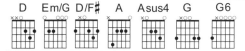

D Em/G D/F♯ A Asus4 G G6

Verse:
D
Lead me, lead me,
Em/G   D/F♯   A   Asus4   A
Lead me to the Rock.
D
Lead me, lead me,
Em/G   A   D
Lead me to the Rock.   [Repeat]

Chorus:
        A   G   D
When the fire comes, when the strong winds blow,
      G   D   A
Precious Saviour, take my hand.
                        G   D
I can count on You, my foundation stone;
      G6   A   D
Rock of ages, You will stand.   [Repeat]

Taken from
BECAUSE OF YOUR LOVE
Brenton Brown
SURCD5124

LET THE CHORDS RING OUT

Brand new day

69.

Johnny Parks, Cathy Parks
& Matt Redman

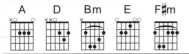

A   D   Bm   E   F#m

Capo 2

Verse 1:
      B(A)
Let the chords ring out, the music play;
   E(D)
I'm thankful, Lord, for this great day.
C#m(Bm)   E(D)
You have changed me, Lord.
    B(A)
I've left behind my guilt and shame
   E(D)
Because You died and rose again.
C#m(Bm)   E(D)
You have changed me, Lord.
           F#(E)
You've changed me, Lord.

Chorus:
          B(A)
It's a brand new day,
        E(D)
It's a brand new day.
   C#m(Bm)
I'll take this risen life You give;
  F#(E)   [1.] B(A) E(D) F#(E)   E(D)
For You I'll live.

Verse 2:
So I'm letting go of all that's gone,
I'm soaking up this bright new dawn,
You have changed me, Lord.
The sun is rising in my life
Because the Son has paid the price;
You have changed me, Lord.
You've changed me, Lord.

Mid section:
G#m(F#m)   E(D)
There's no going back, there's no turning back,
    B(A)   F#(E)
'Cause Christ, You are my future.
G#m(F#m)   E(D)
I'm not going back, I'm not turning back,
    B(A)   F#(E)
'Cause Christ, You are my future.

Taken from
BREAK THE SILENCE
Johnny Parks Band
SURCD5095

LET VOICES SING, LET ANTHEMS RISE

Great Church

Johnny & Cathy Parks
& Matt Redman

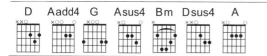

D Aadd4 G Asus4 Bm Dsus4 A

Intro: D Aadd4 G Asus4 D Aadd4 G Aadd4

Verse 1:
```
        D       G       D
Let voices sing, let anthems rise,
            Bm      G          D
The church of Christ has transformed lives!
     Dsus4 D     G         D
Through gene - rations, young and old,
            G       A       D
Who've served the King across the globe.
        G                   D
We join with them in this great quest,
        G                     A
We walk with them through every test.
        Bm      G     D
Because His glory's unsurpassed,
        G           A       D   [1&2:] Aadd4  G  A    [3:] Aadd4  G  Aadd4  D
This is a great church that will last!
```

Verse 2:
The ancient hymns declare His name,
Our hallowed King was without blame;
The helpless Babe, the suffering Christ
Who made Himself the highest price.
This cornerstone will never shake,
This Spire of Hope will never break.
On the Rock, our feet stand fast:
This is a great church that will last!

Verse 3:
We walk on hills of power and peace,
We stand beside the poor and weak.
We'll live by faith and not by sight;
Where there's darkness, we'll bring light.
God's purpose since the dawn of time
Is Christ revealed to all mankind.
Then we'll hear the trumpet blast:
This is a great church that will last!

Ending:
```
G                   A     Asus4
Stir our hearts, pour Your Spirit out again.
G                   A     Asus4   D
Stir our hearts, pour Your Spirit out again.
```

Taken from
BREAK THE SILENCE
Johnny Parks Band
SURCD5095

LIFE'S TOO SHORT TO BE LUKEWARM

(When all is said and done)

Matt Redman

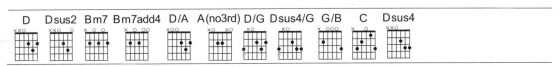

D   Dsus2   Bm7   Bm7add4   D/A   A(no3rd) D/G Dsus4/G   G/B   C   Dsus4

Verse 1:
D   Dsus2   Bm7 Bm7add4
  Life's too short to be luke - warm,
  D/A A(no3rd) D/G   Dsus4/G
This I know,   this I know.
D   Dsus2   Bm7 Bm7add4
  Jesus You can have it   all,
       D/A A(no3rd)   D/G   Dsus4/G
My every breath,   my every breath.

Verse 2.
I need Your power to live this life,
This I know, this I know.
I can't do this by myself,
You're Christ in me,
My only hope, my only hope.

      C
As I walk this broken world,
        G/B
Tune my life to heaven's song,
            D Dsus2
For I am Yours.
      C
And when all is said and done,
        G/B
Tune my life to heaven's song,

         D   D/A
1. Forevermore, forevermore. [1st time]

        D Dsus2   Dsus4   D
2. Forevermore,   forevermore. [2nd time]

        D Dsus2   D Dsus2
3. Forevermore,   I am Yours. [3rd time]
      C
And when all is said and done,
        G/B
Tune my life to heaven's song,
         D
Forevermore.

Taken from
BEAUTIFUL NEWS
Matt Redman
SURCD5071

LORD OF ALL THE EARTH

Johnny Parks & Tim Hughes

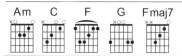

Am   C   F   G   Fmaj7

Verse 1:
Am   C
   Lord of all the earth, Lord of my heart,
F   G
   Let Your purpose be my waking thought;
Am   C   F   G
   Let Your praises be my evening prayer.   [Repeat]

Chorus 1:
          Am
When the day begins, I'll seek Your face,
         Fmaj7   G
When the night-time falls, I'll sing Your praise,
         Am   C   F   G
You're the song of all my days.

Verse 2:
Giving up my dreams, holding onto You;
Trusting all I need is found in You.
Seeking less of me, so there's more of You.

Chorus 2:
          Am
When the day begins, I'll seek Your face,
         Fmaj7   G
When the night-time falls, I'll sing Your praise,
         Am   C   F   G
You're the song of all my days.
         Am   C   F   G
You're the song of all my days.

Mid section:
  C
Singing louder, singing stronger,
  F
Singing louder, singing stronger.
  Am   G   F
Lord of all the earth.
  C
Bow down low to lift You higher,
  F
Bow down low to lift You higher,
  Am   G   F
Lord of all the earth.
      Am   G   F   G
You're Lord of all the earth,
        Am   G   F   G   N.C.(note: A)
You're the Lord of all the earth.

Taken from
BREAK THE SILENCE
Johnny Parks Band
SURCD5095

LORD WE HAVE SEEN

(Shine)

73.
Matt Redman

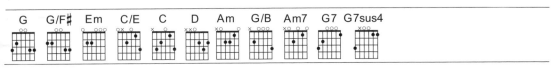

Capo 1

Verse:
```
        G                    G/F♯
Lord we have seen the rising sun
        Em              C/E   Em
Awakening the early dawn,
        C                 G    D
And we're rising up to give You praise.
        G                    G/F♯
Lord we have seen the stars and moon,
                Em              C/E   Em
See how they shine, they shine for You.
        C                 G    D
And You're calling us to do the same.
```

Bridge:
```
        Am
So we rise up with a song,
        G/B
And we rise up with a cry,
        C
And we're giving You our lives.
```

Chorus
```
        G
We will shine like stars in the universe,
        D/F♯
Holding out Your truth in the darkest place.
        Am7
We'll be living for Your glory,
        C                    [Last time to Coda]
Jesus we'll be living for Your glory. [1st time to Verse.]
G
We will burn so bright with Your praise, O God,
        D/F♯
And declare Your light to this broken world.
        Am7
We'll be living for Your glory,
                C
Jesus, we'll be living for Your glory.
```

Mid section:
```
        Am                    G/B
Like the sun so radiantly, sending light for all to see,
        C
Let Your holy church arise.
        Am                    G/B
Exploding into life like a supernova's light,
        C
Set Your holy church on fire.
        G            G7
We will shine,   we will shine. [To Chorus.]
```

Coda:
```
                Am7
So we rise up with a song,
                G/B
And we rise up with a cry,
                C
And we're giving You our lives;
                        G   G7sus4
Jesus, we will shine.
```

Taken from
BEAUTIFUL NEWS
Matt Redman
SURCD5071

LORD WE HAVE SEEN

(Shine)

Verse:

Ab   Ab/G
Lord we have seen the rising sun
  Fm   Db/E Fm
Awakening the early dawn,
    Db   Ab Eb
And we're rising up to give You praise.
   Ab   Ab/G
Lord we have seen the stars and moon,
       Fm   Db/E Fm
See how they shine, they shine for You.
    Db   Ab Eb
And You're calling us to do the same.

Bridge:

   Bbm
So we rise up with a song,
   Ab/C
And we rise up with a cry,
     Db
And we're giving You our lives.

Chorus

    Ab
We will shine like stars in the universe,
    Eb/G
Holding out Your truth in the darkest place.
    Bbm7
We'll be living for Your glory,
     Db   [Last time to Coda]
Jesus we'll be living for Your glory. [1st time to Verse.]
   Ab
We will burn so bright with Your praise, O God,
   Eb/G
And declare Your light to this broken world.
    Bbm7
We'll be living for Your glory,
      Db
Jesus, we'll be living for Your glory.

Mid section:

   Bbm   Ab/C
Like the sun so radiantly, sending light for all to see,
    Db
Let Your holy church arise.
  Bbm   Ab/C
Exploding into life like a supernova's light,
    Db
Set Your holy church on fire.
    Ab   Ab7
We will shine, we will shine. [To Chorus.]

Coda:

    Bbm7
So we rise up with a song,
   Ab/C
And we rise up with a cry,
     Db
And we're giving You our lives;
       Ab Ab7sus4
Jesus, we will shine.

Taken from
BEAUTIFUL NEWS
Matt Redman
SURCD5071

MAJESTY AND PRAISE

(No other God)

Paul Oakley

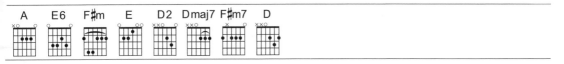

Verse 1:
A   E6   F#m   E   D2
   Majesty and praise ever shall belong to You.
A   E6   F#m   E   D2
   Every star in the sky ever lives to shine for You.
        F#m   E   Dmaj7
No other God shall share Your fame,
        F#m   E   Dmaj7
No other song outlive Your praise.

Chorus:
A   E
   You reign forever,
F#m7   D
   Jesus, my Saviour, my God.
   E   A
I'm living every day for Your name.
        E
For all eternity
F#m7   D
   You'll be my hope and my song,
 E   D   [A]
I lift my voice to crown You with praise.

Verse 2:
Never-ending grace
Ever draws me to Your throne.
Every breath that I take
Shall be Yours and Yours alone.
No other God shall share Your fame,
No other song outlive Your praise.

Taken from
SHOUT FROM THE ROOF
Newday 2006
SURCD5075

MORE THAN THE MOON

(I love You)

Andreana Arganda

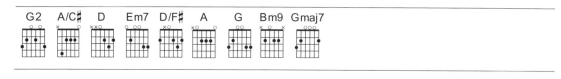

Verse 1:
G2   A/C♯   D   G2
    More than the moon that lights the night,
           A/C♯   D   G2
More than the sunset paints the sky,
           A/C♯   D   G2
More than the flowers and the colour of spring,
       Em7 D/F♯   G2
You have captured my gaze.

Verse 2:
More than the birds and the songs they sing,
More than the notes played by a symphony,
More than a choir and its harmony
Your voice beckons me.

Chorus:
        A   G   D
You are Jesus, You are Saviour, You are Lord;
        A   G   Bm9 A/C♯
You are everything my heart is longing for.
     G   D/F♯   Em7 D/F♯   G   D/F♯
And I love You, yes, I love You, but I love You,
       Em7   D/F♯   Gmaj7
1. Yes, I love You, but I love You. [Repeat v.2]
       Em7   D/F♯   G D/F♯ Em7 D/F♯   G2
2. Yes, I love You, but I love You,   yes, I love You. You are Jesus . . .

Last chorus:
        A   G   D
You are Jesus, You are Saviour, You are Lord;
        A   G   Bm9 A/C♯
You are everything my heart is longing for.
     G   D/F♯   Em7 D/F♯   G   D/F♯
And I love You, yes, I love You, but I love You,
      Em7 D/F♯   G2   D/F♯
Yes, I love You, Lord, I love You,
      Em7 D/F♯   G2 D/F♯ Em7
Yes, I love You, Lord, I love You
D/F♯   G2
    Lord, I love You.

Taken from
THE PEOPLE'S ALBUM 3
SURCD5140

MY SOUL IS WEAK

(Clinging to the cross)

Tim Hughes
& Martin Smith

Em Gmaj7 Cmaj7 Am7 G D G/D

Capo 3

Verse 1:
```
Em          Gmaj7
   My soul is weak, my heart is numb,
Cmaj7       Em          Gmaj7      Cmaj7
   I cannot see, but still my hope is found in You.
Em          Gmaj7       Cmaj7
   I hold on tightly, You will never let me go,
Am7         G           D
   For Jesus, You will never fail,
Am7      G          D
   Jesus, You will never fail.
```

Chorus:
```
G
Simply to the cross I cling,
D                          Am7
Letting go of all earthly things,
   Cmaj7        D
I'm clinging to the cross.
G
Mercy's found a way for me,
D
Hope is here as I am free,
Am7
Jesus, You are all I need;   [Not 2nd time]
   Cmaj7           D [Em  G/D  Cmaj7  Em  G/D  Cmaj7]
I'm clinging to the cross.
```

Verse 2:
Even darkness is as light to You, my Lord,
So light the way and lead me home -
To that place where every tear is wiped away:
For Jesus, You will never fail,
Jesus, You will never fail.

```
         Em   G     Cmaj7  Am7
What a Saviour, what a story,
            Em   G   Cmaj7     Am7
You were crucified,   but now You are alive.
    Em    G          Cmaj7  Am7
So amazing,    such a mystery,
            Em   G   Cmaj7     Am7
You were crucified,   but now You are alive.
```

Taken from
HOLDING NOTHING BACK
Tim Hughes
SURCD5068

MY SOUL IS WEAK

(Clinging to the cross)

Verse 1:
Gm   B♭maj7
   My soul is weak, my heart is numb,
E♭maj7   Gm   B♭maj7   E♭maj7
   I cannot see, but still my hope is found in You.
Gm   B♭maj7   E♭maj7
   I hold on tightly, You will never let me go,
Cm7   B♭   F
   For Jesus, You will never fail,
Cm7   B♭   F
   Jesus, You will never fail.

Chorus:
B♭
Simply to the cross I cling,
F   Cm7
Letting go of all earthly things,
     E♭maj7   F
I'm clinging to the cross.
B♭
Mercy's found a way for me,
F
Hope is here as I am free,
Cm7
Jesus, You are all I need;   [Not 2nd time]
    E♭maj7   F [Gm B♭/F E♭maj7 Gm B♭/F E♭maj7]
I'm clinging to the cross.

Verse 2:
Even darkness is as light to You, my Lord,
So light the way and lead me home -
To that place where every tear is wiped away:
For Jesus, You will never fail,
Jesus, You will never fail.

       Gm   B♭   E♭maj7 Cm7
What a Saviour, what a story,
           Gm   B♭   E♭maj7   Cm7
You were crucified,   but now You are alive.
      Gm   B♭   E♭maj7 Cm7
So amazing,   such a mystery,
           Gm   B♭   E♭maj7   Cm7
You were crucified,   but now You are alive.

Taken from
HOLDING NOTHING BACK
Tim Hughes
SURCD5068

NATIONS BOW

(Holy is the Lamb)

D   Asus4   G2   Em7   Bm7

Capo 2

Verse 1:
D   Asus4
  Nations bow, heavens sing
G2   Em7 Bm7   Asus4
  Glory to our God and King.
D   Asus4
  All earth shouts, people sing,
G2   Em7   Bm7
  With one voice we all praise Him.

Bridge:
G2 Bm7 Asus4 G2 Bm7 Asus4 D
Al - le - luia,   al - le - lu - ia,
G2 Bm7 Asus4 G2 Bm7 Asus4 [Last time D]
Al - le - luia,   Al - le - luia.

Verse 2:
Holiness adorns Your house,
Love abounds in where You are found.
In Your hands, mercy's gift,
G2   Em7 Bm7 Asus4
  Grace poured out all over sin.

Chorus:
G2 D   Bm7   Asus4
Holy is the Lamb, the One who gave His life.
G2 D   Bm7   Asus4   G2 Asus4 G2 Asus4
Holy is the Lamb, for love's the reason He died and rose again.

Verse 3:
Mighty Saviour, great I Am,
Worthy is the risen Lamb.
It's You we enthrone, sat at the right hand;
Now to join in heaven's song,
G2   Em7 Bm7   Asus4
  Sing alleluia, alleluia.

Coda:

Holy, holy, holy is the Lamb.

Taken from
THE PEOPLE'S ALBUM, 3,
SURCD5140

NEVERENDING

David Crowder, Jack Parker,
Jeremy Bush & Mike Hogan

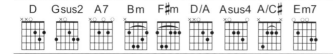

D Gsus2 A7 Bm F#m D/A Asus4 A/C# Em7

Verse:
Eb(D)   Absus2(Gsus2)   Bb7(A7)
Neverending, always,   You will never
Eb(D)   Absus2(Gsus2)   Bb7(A7)
End because You're always,   neverending.
Eb(D)   Absus2(Gsus2)   Bb7(A7)
You were there before there   was beginning.
Eb(D)   Absus2(Gsus2)   Bb7(A7)
Always You were, You are   neverending.

Bridge:
Cm(Bm)   Gm(F#m)
Here, You are now,
          Cm(Bm)
With us here.
          Gm(F#m)   Eb/Bb(D/A)
We are found   in You.

Chorus:
Eb(D)   Bbsus4(Asus4)
   And this makes all the difference,
Absus2(Gsus2) Bbsus4(Asus4)
   This changes everything,
Eb(D)   Bbsus4(Asus4)
   Making our whole existence
Absus2(Gsus2)   Bbsus4(Asus4)
   Worth something. So we sing:
Eb(D)
La, la, la, la, la, la, la, la.

[Second time:]
Eb(D)   Absus2(Gsus2)   Bb(A)
La, la, la, la, la, la,   la, la.
Cm(Bm)   Bb/D(A/C#)   Absus2(Gsus2)   Bb(A)
La, la,   la, la,   la, la,   la, la.
Eb(D)   Fm7(Em7)   Absus2(Gsus2)   Bb(A)
La, la,   la, la,   la, la,   la, la.
Cm(Bm)   Bb/D(A/C#)   Absus2(Gsus2)   Bb(A)   Eb(D)
La, la,   la, la,   la, la, la, la, la.   la, la,   la.

Taken from
REMEDY
David Crowder Band
SURCD5101

The Name Of The Lord Is To Be Praised   **Andreana Arganda & Beth Redman**

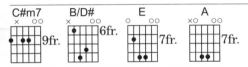

```
C#m7        B/D#           E            A
x  oo       x  oo        o  oo        xo  oo
      9fr.        6fr.        7fr.         7fr.
```

Intro: C#m7 B/D# E E   x4

Verse 1:
```
E    B/D#      C#m7
   No longer in chains
A              C#m7  B/D#    A
I have found my freedom      in You
E    B/D#      C#m7
   No more am I bound
        A        C#m7            B/D#    A
You've taken my shame and my sorrow away
B     C#m7          A
   I will walk with my head lifted up
B            C#m7                A
   The old has gone and the new has come
```

Chorus:
```
                  C#m7  B/D#   E
And the name of the Lord is to be praised
                  C#m7  B/D#   E
The name of the Lord is to be praised
                  C#m7  B/D#   E
The name of the Lord is to be praised
                  C#m7  B/D#   E
The name of the Lord is to be praised
```

Verse 2:
```
E  B/D#      C#m7
   Alone and afraid
A              C#m7       B/D#    A
I was lost, in need of Your amazing grace
E          B/D#   C#m7
   You came into my life
A              C#m7     B/D#          A
Poured out Your unfailing love and Your truth
B      C#m7          A
   By Your grace I stand justified
B            C#m7       A
   Because of You, have eternal life
```

Taken from
PRECIOUS
Soul Sista
SURCD5015

NOW COME ON EVERYBODY

Love, come take me home

Tré & Tori Sheppard, Mark Prentice,
Paul Baker, Jonny Ravn & Steve Evans

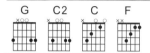

G   C2   C   F

Verse 1:
G   C2
   Now, come on everybody,
                       C
If you're tired of your old ways,
              G
Come back home.
                         C2
Bring your sons and your daughters,
                   C
Come down to the water,
                    G
And come back home.

Chorus:
F   C   G
Love, come take me home.
F   C   G
Love, come take me home.
F   C   G
Love, come take me home.
F   C   G
Love, come take me home.

Verse 2:
Now, if you're dead on arrival,
You got stuck in survival,
Come back home.
If your heart's on the highway,
And you're sick of this old game,
Come back home.

Verse 3:
I got so tired of this battle
Between my angels and devils,
I had to come back home.
Yeah, 'cause I'm a believer
In love when I see her,
Come take me home.

Verse 4:
Now, if you're tired of the battle,
Between your angels and devils,
Come back home.
Hey, can I get a believer,
To tune love to your receiver?
Come back home.

Taken from
AS SURE AS THE STARS
Onehundredhours
SURCD5089

Charles Wesley (1707-88)
New music & additional text: David Crowder & Jack Parker

G   Dsus4   D   C   Gsus4   D/G   Csus2   G/B   Am7   Am7add4

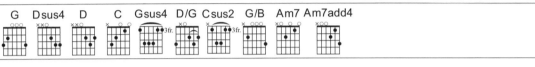

Verse 1:
  G
O, for a thousand tongues to sing
                Dsus4
My great Redeemer's praise,
D   G   C
The glories of my God and King,
  G   D   G   Gsus4   D/G
The triumphs of His grace.
  G
My gracious Master and my God,
       Dsus4
Assist me to proclaim,
D   G   C
To spread throughout the earth abroad,
  G   D   G   Gsus4   D/G
The honours of Thy name.

Chorus:
G   Csus2   G/B   Am7   G
So come on, and sing out, let our anthem grow loud.
      Csus2   G/B   Am7add4
There is one   great love,
      Csus2   G/B   Am7add4
There is one   great love,
      Csus2   G/B   Am7add4   G   [1.,2.,3.,5.] Gsus4   D/G
There is one   great love,   Jesus.

Verse 2:
Jesus, the name that charms our fears,
That bids our sorrows cease.
'Tis music in the sinner's ears,
'Tis life and health and peace.
He breaks the power of cancelled sin,
He sets the prisoner free,
His blood can make the foulest clean,
His blood availed for me.

Verse 3:
He speaks, and listening to His voice,
New life the dead receive.
The mournful, broken hearts rejoice,
The humble poor believe.
Glory to God, and praise and love
Be ever, ever given
By saints below and saints above;
The church in earth and heaven.

Mid section:
G
There are so few words that never grow old.
There are so few words that never grow old, Jesus, Jesus.
Jesus, Jesus.

Verse 4:
Jesus, the name that charms our fears,
That bids our sorrows cease.
'Tis music in the sinner's ears,
'Tis life and health and peace.

Taken from
REMEDY
David Crowder Band
SURCD5101
and
GOD OF THIS CITY
Passion
SURCD5126

O LORD, WILL YOU STRETCH OUR HEARTS?   82.

Walls

Johnny & Cathy Parks

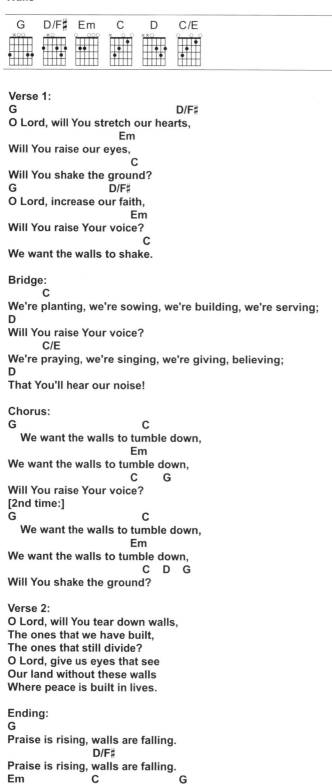

G   D/F♯   Em   C   D   C/E

Verse 1:
```
G                              D/F♯
O Lord, will You stretch our hearts,
                      Em
Will You raise our eyes,
                      C
Will You shake the ground?
G              D/F♯
O Lord, increase our faith,
                      Em
Will You raise Your voice?
                      C
We want the walls to shake.
```

Bridge:
```
      C
We're planting, we're sowing, we're building, we're serving;
D
Will You raise Your voice?
      C/E
We're praying, we're singing, we're giving, believing;
D
That You'll hear our noise!
```

Chorus:
```
G                      C
   We want the walls to tumble down,
                  Em
We want the walls to tumble down,
                  C      G
Will You raise Your voice?
[2nd time:]
G                      C
   We want the walls to tumble down,
                  Em
We want the walls to tumble down,
                  C   D   G
Will You shake the ground?
```

Verse 2:
O Lord, will You tear down walls,
The ones that we have built,
The ones that still divide?
O Lord, give us eyes that see
Our land without these walls
Where peace is built in lives.

Ending:
```
G
Praise is rising, walls are falling.
              D/F♯
Praise is rising, walls are falling.
Em          C          G
Praise is rising, walls are falling down.
```

Taken from
BREAK THE SILENCE
Johnny Parks Band
SURCD5095

O PRECIOUS SIGHT
(The wonder of the cross)

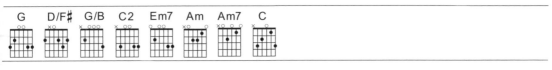

G   D/F♯   G/B   C2   Em7   Am   Am7   C

Capo 1

Verse 1:
```
        G          D/F♯   G
```
O precious sight, my Saviour stands,
```
        G/B
```
Dying for me with outstretched hands.
```
        C2      D/F♯  Em7
```
O precious sight; I love to gaze,
```
       Am     D/F♯  Em7
```
Remembering salvation day,
```
       Am     D/F♯  G
```
Remembering salvation day.

Verse 2:
Though my eyes linger on this scene,
May passing time and years not steal
The power with which it impacts me,
The freshness of its mystery,
The freshness of its mystery.

Chorus:
```
G                      D/F♯
```
May I never lose the wonder,
```
     Am7        G
```
The wonder of the cross.
```
     Em7        D/F♯
```
May I see it like the first time,
```
         Am7        Em7
```
Standing as a sinner lost.
```
             C        G/B
```
Undone my mercy and left speechless,
```
         Am7               Em7
```
Watching wide-eyed at the cost.
```
     C    D/F♯   Em7
```
May I never lose the wonder,
```
     Am      D/F♯  G
```
The wonder of the cross.

Verse 3:
Behold, the God - Man crucified,
The perfect sinless sacrifice.
As blood ran down those nails and wood,
History was split in two,
History was split in two.

Verse 4:
Behold, the empty wooden tree,
His body gone, alive and free.
We sing with everlasting joy
For sin and death have been destroyed,
Sin and death have been destroyed.

Taken from
PAINTING THE INVISIBLE
Vicky Beeching
SURCD5091

O PRECIOUS SIGHT
(The wonder of the cross)

Verse 1:
      Ab   Eb/G   Ab
O precious sight, my Saviour stands,
        Ab/C
Dying for me with outstretched hands.
         Db2   Eb/G   Fm7
O precious sight; I love to gaze,
       Abm   Eb/G Fm7
Remembering salvation day,
       Abm   Eb/G Ab
Remembering salvation day.

Verse 2:
Though my eyes linger on this scene,
May passing time and years not steal
The power with which it impacts me,
The freshness of its mystery,
The freshness of its mystery.

Chorus:
Ab   Eb/G
May I never lose the wonder,
    Abm7   Ab
The wonder of the cross.
     Fm7   Eb/G
May I see it like the first time,
       Abm7   Fm7
Standing as a sinner lost.
         Db   Ab/C
Undone my mercy and left speechless,
     Abm7   Fm7
Watching wide-eyed at the cost.
    Db   Eb/G   Fm7
May I never lose the wonder,
   Abm   Eb/G Ab
The wonder of the cross.

Verse 3:
Behold, the God - Man crucified,
The perfect sinless sacrifice.
As blood ran down those nails and wood,
History was split in two,
History was split in two.

Verse 4:
Behold, the empty wooden tree,
His body gone, alive and free.
We sing with everlasting joy
For sin and death have been destroyed,
Sin and death have been destroyed.

Taken from
PAINTING THE INVISIBLE
Vicky Beeching
SURCD5091

OH, YOU'VE BEEN SO GOOD TO ME

Here we go

Ben Cantelon

Verse:
A
Oh, You've been so good to me.
D
Yeah, I cannot help but sing.
E
Oh, I think we all agree
             D
That it's time to dance, it's time to sing,
     E
It's time to worship the King.
         A
So here we go. Here we go.

Chorus:
          G
You've been so good to me,
    D
Now I can dance and sing.
      A
So here we go. Here we go.
      G
For You have set us free,
    D
Now we can dance and sing.
      A
For You are good.

Mid section:
G
   And we will not stay silent,
D   A
   But shout aloud that You are good.
G
   No, we will not stay silent,
D   E   G
   But shout aloud as we all dance and sing.

Taken from
LIVING FOR YOUR GLORY
Soul Survivor Live 2007
SURCD5108

O KNEEL ME DOWN AGAIN

Humble King

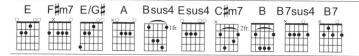

E   F#m7 E/G#   A   Bsus4 Esus4 C#m7   B   B7sus4 B7

Verse:
```
E                 F#m7   E/G#  A     Bsus4  E      Esus4  E
  O kneel me down  again,      here at   Your feet;
E                    F#m7    E/G#  A     Bsus4  E      Esus4  E
  Show me how much You love         humility.
E              F#m7  E/G#  A     Bsus4     C#m7  B  A
  Oh Spirit, be the star      that leads me to
   E/G#    F#m7         B7sus4  B7        E   Esus4  E
The humble heart of love        I see in You.
```

Chorus:
```
                 A          E/G#
'Cause You are the God of the broken,
   F#m7            B
The friend of the weak.
                 A          E/G#
You wash the feet of the weary,
   F#m7             B
Embrace the ones in need.
               A          E/G#
I want to be like You, Jesus,
   F#m7             B
To have this heart in me.
              F#m7       E/G#
You are the God of the humble,
    A       B7          E  Esus4   E
You are the humble King.
```

Ending:
```
            A          E/G#
I want to be like You, Jesus,
   F#m7             B
To have this heart in me.        [X3]
              F#m7       E/G#
You are the God of the humble,
    A       B7          E  Esus4   E
You are the humble King.
```

Taken from
BECAUSE OF YOUR LOVE
Brenton Brown
SURCD5124

ON CHRIST THE SOLID ROCK WE STAND

Rock of ages, You will stand

Paul Baloche & Brenton Brown

Amaj7 F#m7   E   D2   A   Esus4 F#m7(add4)

Verse 1:
Amaj7
On Christ the solid rock we stand;
F#m7
All other ground is sinking sand:
E
Great is Your faithfulness,
   D2   Amaj7
Great is Your love, O God.
Our hope is built on nothing less
F#m7
Than Jesus' blood and righteousness:
E
Great is Your faithfulness,
   D2   Amaj7
Great is Your love, O God.

Chorus:
     D2   A
Rock of ages, You will stand.
     D2   F#m7
Our foundation 'til the end.
    D2   F#m7
Never failing, God unchanging:
    D2 Esus4   Amaj7   F#m7
Rock of ages,   You will stand.

Verse 2:
When darkness seems to hide Your face,
I rest on Your unchanging grace:
Great is Your faithfulness,
Great is Your love, O God.
In every high and stormy gale,
My anchor holds within the veil:
Great is Your faithfulness,
Great is Your love, O God.

Verse 3:
Amaj7
On Christ the solid rock we stand;
F#m7
All other ground is sinking sand:
E
Great is Your faithfulness,
   D2   F#m7(add4)
Great is Your love, O God.

Taken from
BECAUSE OF YOUR LOVE
Brenton Brown
SURCD5124

ONE DAY EVERY VOICE WILL SING

(Join the song)

Vicky Beeching
& Ed Cash

D D/F# G2 Bm7 F#m7 Em7 A/C# A7 Am/C G2/B A

Capo 3

Verse 1:
D   D/F#   G2
One day every voice will sing,
Bm7   F#m7   G2
Every beggar, prince and king,
D   D/F#   G2
Every nation, tongue and tribe,
     Bm7   F#m7   G2   Em7
Every ocean in between will cry,   will cry.

Verse 2:
Gathered round the throne above,
We'll be swept up in the melody,
Hearts will overflow with love,
We'll be singing out a symphony

Chorus:
       D
Praise God from whom all blessings flow,
     A/C#
Praise Him, all creatures here below.
  Bm7   G
To Him all the glory belongs.
     D
Praise Him above, you heavenly host,
     A/C#
Praise Father, Son and Holy Ghost,
    Bm7   G
Let all the earth sing along;
  G2   D Em7 Bm7 A7 D Em7 Bm7 A7
1.   Come join the song.

Mid section:
  G2   Em7
2.   Come join the song that fills eternity,
  G2   A7
Sung throughout all history,
  Em7   D/F#   G2
As angels shout and kings lay down their crowns,
         Gm
We bow down.
     D/F#   A/C#
Praise God from whom all blessings flow,
    Am/C   G2/B
Praise Him, all creatures here below.
     D   A/C#
Praise Him above you heavenly host,
    Am/C   G2/B
Praise Father, Son and Holy Ghost.

Coda:
G2   D Em7
  Come join the song,   (sing along.)
Bm7   A7   D Em7 Bm7 A D
  Come join the song.

Copyright © 2006 Thankyou Music admin by kingswaysongs.com tym@kingsway.co.uk for UK & Europe &
Alletrop Music admin by CopyCare PO Box 77, Hailsham, BN27 3EF, UK, music@copycare.com.
Chorus adapted from, The Doxology, Words by Thomas Ken, Public Domain. Used by Permission.

Taken from
PAINTING THE INVISIBLE
Vicky Beeching
SURCD5091

ONE DAY EVERY VOICE WILL SING

(Join the song)

87.

Vicky Beeching
& Ed Cash

Verse 1:
```
F          F/A        Bb2
One day every voice will sing,
Dm7        Am7        Bb2
Every beggar, prince and king,
F          F/A        Bb2
Every nation, tongue and tribe,
    Dm7        Am7       Bb2      Gm7
Every ocean in between will cry,   will cry.
```

Verse 2:
Gathered round the throne above,
We'll be swept up in the melody,
Hearts will overflow with love,
We'll be singing out a symphony

Chorus:
```
         F
Praise God from whom all blessings flow,
     C/E
Praise Him, all creatures here below.
    Dm7              Bb
To Him all the glory belongs.
         F
Praise Him Above, you heavenly host,
         C/E
Praise Father, Son and Holy Ghost,
    Dm7              Bb
Let all the earth sing along;
    Bb2          [1.F  Gm7  Dm7  C7  F  Gm7  Dm7  C7]
1.   Come join the song.
```

Mid section:
```
    Bb2              Gm7
2.    Come join the song that fills eternity,
    Bb2              C7
Sung throughout all history,
    Gm7              F/A              Bb2
As angels shout and kings lay down their crowns,
                     Gm
We bow down.
    F/A                          C/E
Praise God from whom all blessings flow,
    C/Eb                    Bb2/F
Praise Him, all creatures here below.
    F                      C/E
Praise Him Above you heavenly host,
    C/Eb                    Bb2/F
Praise Father, Son and Holy Ghost.
```

Coda:
```
Bb2              F   Gm7
   Come join the song,     (sing along.)
Dm7      C7     F  Gm7  Dm7  C  F
   Come join the song.
```

Taken from
PAINTING THE INVISIBLE
Vicky Beeching
SURCD5091

ONE MOMENT THE SKIES ARE BLUE

To the God above

James Gregory & Guy Bastable

D C G Am Em D/F♯

Capo 4(G)

Verse 1:

F♯(D)   E(C)
  One moment the skies are blue
                    B(G)
And everything is clear.
F♯(D)   E(C)
  Then storm-clouds are rolling in;
                  B(G)
Our God - are You still here?
F♯(D)   E(C)
  Though all of our words fall short
            B(G)
In trying to explain,
F♯(D)   E(C)
  You're good, and we turn to You,
      C♯m(Am)   F♯(D)
Surrendering again.

Chorus:

             B(G)   F♯(D)
To the God above all circumstance,
            E(C)   F♯(D)
Whose ways are higher than our ways,
      C♯m(Am)   G♯m(Em)
We lift our eyes and see Your face
          E(C)
And run to You.

Verse 2:

We trust in Your majesty,
Your good and perfect will.
Our wisdom is foolishness,
Our strength alone will fail.
Though You're still a mystery,
Of one thing we are sure:
You're good and we turn to You,
Surrendering our all.

Mid section:

  G♯m(Em) E(C) B(G)   F♯/A♯(D/F♯)
We run   to You, we run to You.
  G♯m(Em)   E(C)   B(G) F♯(D)
God, no-one else will do, we run to You.
  G♯m(Em) E(C) B(G)   F♯/A♯(D/F♯)
We run   to You, we run to You.
  G♯m(Em)   E(C)   B(G) F♯(D)
God, no-one else will do, we run to You.

ON THE AFRICAN PLAINS

(Friend of the poor)

Paul Baloche, Steven Curtis-Chapman, Stuart Garrard, Israel Houghton,
Tim Hughes, Graham Kendrick, Andy Park, Matt Redman,
Martin Smith, Michael W. Smith, Chris Tomlin, Darlene Zschech

Am7 Fmaj7 G D/F♯ C G/B Dm7 Fmaj7/A Em Esus4 E

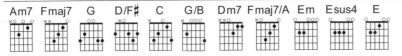

Verse 1:
     Am7
On the African plains,
                     Fmaj7
A young mother weeps for her hungry child,

She prays he'll survive.
Am7
Tearfilled eyes,
               Fmaj7
She looks up to heaven, calls Your name,

She pours out her pain.
G   D/F♯
   You know her name,
       Fmaj7
And You hear her cries.

Chorus:
            C   G/B
Friend of the poor,   help me through the night,
                Dm7   Fmaj7
Help me in the fight,   come to my rescue.
            C   G/B
Friend of the poor,   take this skin and bones,

[1.& 2.]   Dm7   Fmaj7
Make this heart a home;   Come to my rescue,
              Am7   G   Fmaj7/A   Am7   G   Fmaj7/A
Friend of the poor.
[Last time]   Dm7   F Fmaj7
Make this heart a home;   Come to my rescue,
              Am7   G   Fmaj7/A   Am7   G   Fmaj7/A
Friend of the poor.

Verse 2:
On the streets of L.A.
An old man lies in his cardboard home;
He feels so alone.
With tear-stained eyes
He looks up to heaven
And prays a prayer:
"Is there anyone there?"
You know his name and You hear his cries.

Mid section:
   Em
It's getting dark, it's getting late,
  Fmaj7   Am7   Dm7
It's cold outside the rich man's gate;
     C   Esus4   E   Fmaj7
And I'm wondering, do eou have any friends around here?

Who are friends of the poor. . .

Taken from
COMPASSIONART

OUR GOD IS ENDLESS

90.

Our God is mighty

Johnny Parks, Cathy Parks
& Claire Hamilton

A D Bm E Asus4 E/G# F#m

Intro: A D Bm E

Verse 1:
A   D
Our God is endless, our God is ageless,
   Bm   E
There's nothing that He can't do.
A   D
Our God is gracious, our God is selfless,
   Bm   E
There's nothing that He can't do.
A   D
Our God is famous, our God is fearless,
   Bm   E
There's nothing that He can't do.
A   D
Our God is living, our God is moving,
   Bm   E
There's nothing that He can't do.

Chorus:
    Asus4 A   E/G#
Our God is migh - ty, He's over all things,
   F#m   E   D
Our great Redeemer, there's no-one like You.
     Asus4 A   E/G#
All power and glo - ry are Yours forever:
    F#m   E   D
And there's nothing that You can't do.

Verse 2:
Our God was human, our God was humble,
There's nothing that He can't do.
Our God was broken, our God has suffered,
There's nothing that He can't do.
Our God is risen, death is defeated,
There's nothing that He can't do.
Seated in glory, reigning forever,
There's nothing that He can't do.

Ending:
    F#m   E   D
And there's nothing that You can't do,
    F#m   E/G# D A
No, there's nothing that You can't do.

1

Copyright © 2007 Thankyou Music/Adm by worshiptogether.com songs
excl. UK & Europe, adm. by kingswaysongs.com tym@kingsway.co.uk. Used by permission.

Taken from
BREAK THE SILENCE
Johnny Parks Band
SURCD5095

PRAISE HIM SUN AND MOON

(Shout praise)

Paul Baloche, Steven Curtis-Chapman, Stuart Garrard, Israel Houghton,
Tim Hughes, Graham Kendrick, Toby Mac, Andy Park, Matt Redman,
Martin Smith, Michael W. Smith, Chris Tomlin, Darlene Zschech

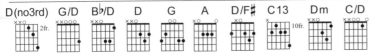

D(no3rd) G/D Bb/D D G A D/F# C13 Dm C/D

Capo 2:

Verse 1:

D(no3rd)
Praise Him sun and moon, praise Him shining stars,

All created things, made in His command.

Governments and kings, nations of the earth,

Gather young and old, to worship.
G/D   Bb/D
Let ev'rything that has breath

Chorus:
                D G   D A
Shout praise   to His name,
            D G   D A
To the name above all names.
         D G   D A
Sing glory,   hallelujah,
       D G   A   D
Hallelujah to His name. [Last time: Shout praise.]
D/F# G   D/F# G   A   [1. N.C.   C13   N.C.   C13   N.C.]
King Je - sus,   Je - sus be praised.

Verse 2:
Underneath our feet, there's a shaking,
As the church awakes, to it's calling.
Hope is rising strong, freedom's coming,
Heaven and earth unite, in worship:
Let everything that has breath . . .

Mid section:
Dm /// Dm /// C/D /// Bb/D ///

     Dm
Say what you want, what you know, we're 'bout to make His kingdom grow.
C/D   Bb/D
What you want, what you know, we're 'bout to make His kingdom grow.
     D(no3rd)   C/D   Bb/D
The King is coming, King is coming,   let everything that has breath praise Him. [Repeat x3]
     D(no3rd)   C/D   Bb/D
The King is coming, King is coming,   let everything that has breath shout praise. . .

Taken from
COMPASSIONART

PRAISE HIM SUN AND MOON

(Shout praise)

Paul Baloche, Steven Curtis-Chapman, Stuart Garrard, Israel Houghton,
Tim Hughes, Graham Kendrick, Toby Mac, Andy Park, Matt Redman,
Martin Smith, Michael W. Smith, Chris Tomlin, Darlene Zschech

Verse 1:

E(no3rd)
  Praise Him sun and moon, praise Him shining stars,

All created things, made in His command.

Governments and kings, nations of the earth,

Gather young and old, to worship.
A/E   C/E
  Let ev'rything that has breath

Chorus:
            E A   E B
Shout praise   to His name,
         E A   E B
To the name above all names.
      E A   E B
Sing glory,   hallelujah,
     E A   B   E
Hallelujah to His name. [Last time: Shout praise.]
E/G♯ A   E/G♯ A   B   [1. N.C. D13 N.C. D13 N.C.]
King Je - sus,   Je - sus be praised.

Verse 2:
Underneath our feet, there's a shaking,
As the church awakes, to it's calling.
Hope is rising strong, freedom's coming,
Heaven and earth unite, in worship:
Let everything that has breath . . .

Mid section:
Em / / /   Em / / /   D/E / / /   C/E / / /

     Em
Say what you want, what you know, we're 'bout to make His kingdom grow.
D/E   C/E
What you want, what you know, we're 'bout to make His kingdom grow.
   E(no3rd)   D/E   C/E
The King is coming, King is coming,   let everything that has breath praise Him. [Repeat x3]
   E(no3rd)   D/E   C/E
The King is coming, King is coming,   let everything that has breath shout praise. . .

RISING UP LIKE A TIDE

Victorious

Johnny Parks & Matt Redman

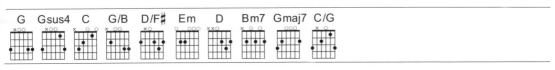

G   Gsus4   C   G/B   D/F♯   Em   D   Bm7   Gmaj7   C/G

Capo 3

Intro: B♭(G) B♭sus4(Gsus4) B♭(G) B♭sus4(Gsus4)

Verse 1:
      B♭(G)   E♭(C)
Rising up like a tide,
     B♭/D(G/B)   E♭(C)
It's a sound we can't hide:
         F/A(D/F♯)
This is it.
         Gm(Em) E♭(C)
Who can stop this noise?
       B♭(G)   E♭(C)
See the church through the world
        B♭/D(G/B)   E♭(C)
With the saints of the past
         F/A(D/F♯)
Standing strong.
         Gm(Em) E♭(C)
Who can stop this noise?

Bridge:
E♭(C)   F(D)
Break the silence,
Dm7(Bm7) E♭(C)
Lift your   voice.
E♭(C)   F(D)
Break the silence,
Dm7(Bm7) E♭(C)
Lift your   voice.

Chorus:
B♭(G)   E♭(C)
Can you hear the sound?
       F(D)
Victorious!
       E♭(C)
Victorious!
    B♭(G)   E♭(C)
The saints go marching on,
         F(D)
Your praise in us,
      E♭(C)B♭maj7(Gmaj7)   E♭/B♭(C/G)   B♭maj7(Gmaj7)   E♭/B♭(C/G)   [Last time:] B♭maj7(Gmaj7)
Victorious!

Verse 2:
The drums, the dance,
The cry of our hearts rising up;
Who can stop this noise?
Oh, the prayers, the psalms,
The works of our hands are the song;
Who can stop this noise?

Taken from
BREAK THE SILENCE
Johnny Parks Band
SURCD5095

SEARCH ME AND TRY ME

93.

Andy Smith

Am7 Em7 Dm7 Fmaj7 B♭maj7 F G C/B Gsus4 Fm Fm6

Capo 5
Verse 1:
```
        Am7
Search me and try me,
           Em7
Know me completely
    Dm7
And reveal the ways in me.
              Am7
In my darkest of moments,
                  Em7
Your light will inspire me
       Dm7
And consume what's blinding me.
              Am7
'Cause I can't escape You,
        Em7
I can't outrun You,
      Fmaj7              B♭maj7
For Your love has captured me.
             Am7
So hold me in Your ways,
         Em7
Guide me with Your hand
     Dm7
To the place I want to be.
```

Chorus:
```
F              G
  Awesome God,
       C              C/B              F
You are wiser than, greater than I know.
       G
Your design
       Am7          Gsus4
Was to make me in that secret place.
F        G
  Holy One,
            C              C/B              F
Would You lead me in the way that lasts forever,
    Fm     Fm6    C
Forever    with    You.
```

Taken from
BREATHE
Andy Smith
SURCD5073

SEARCH ME AND TRY ME

Verse 1:
```
          Dm7
Search me and try me,
              Am7
Know me completely
    Gm7
And reveal the ways in me.
                  Dm7
In my darkest of moments,
                        Am7
Your light will inspire me
        Gm7
And consume what's blinding me.
                  Dm7
'Cause I can't escape You,
        Am7
I can't outrun You,
    Bbmaj7              Ebmaj7
For Your love has captured me.
              Dm7
So hold me in Your ways,
              Am7
Guide me with Your hand
      Gm7
To the place I want to be.
```

Chorus:
```
Bb            C
   Awesome God,
        F         F/E           Bb
You are wiser than, greater than I know.
              C
Your design
        Dm7          Csus4
Was to make me in that secret place.
Bb        C
   Holy One,
              F          F/E          Bb
Would You lead me in the way that lasts forever,
    Bbm   Bbm6  F
Forever   with   You.
```

Taken from
BREATHE
Andy Smith
SURCD5073

SEE THE MORNING

(Rejoice)

Chris Tomlin, Ed Cash
& Jesse Reeves

94.

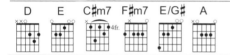

D E C#m7 F#m7 E/G# A

Verse 1:
```
        D              E
See the morning, see it rising
C#m7            F#m7
Over the mountains high.
        D          E          F#m7  E/G#  A
See the mercy in the mighty hand of God.
        D              E
Living water come and fill us,
     C#m7         F#m7
Only You can satisfy.
            D           E
Turn our sorrow into singing
        D     E
The song of life.
```

Chorus:
```
     A       E/G#
Rejoice, rejoice,
     F#m7                D
And sing with the angel voices.
     A       E/G#
Rejoice, rejoice,
     F#m7               D     A
All heaven and earth rejoice.
```

Verse 2:
```
Lord, Your strength is a tower,
The righteous run into.
Lord, Your love is a banner over us.
And we hold on to the promise,
That Your hold on us is true.
There's no other like You, Jesus,
No one like You.
```

Mid section:
```
     E                C#m7
Always, again I say rejoice.
     F#m7             D
Always, again I say rejoice.
     E                C#m7
Always, again I say rejoice.
     F#m7       D
Always, always.
```

Taken from
SEE THE MORNING
Chris Tomlin
SURCD5084

SEND YOUR RAIN

Brenton Brown

D G Bm A Em7 A7sus2 Dsus4

Verse:
      D
Send Your rain, send Your rain,
     G   D   Bm   A
Let Your healing fall on our hearts again,
        D   Em7   D
'Cause we are dry, we're crying out:
       G   D   Bm   A
Saviour, send the streams that will break the drought.
        D
Send Your rain.

Chorus:
         G   D
Generous God, You pour out
       G   Bm A
Tender mercies on Your children.
       G   D
In Your grace, hear us now,
      A   G   D
Send Your rain, send Your rain.
         G   D
Generous God, You pour out
       G   Bm A
Tender mercies on Your children.
       G   D
In Your grace, hear us now,
      A   G   D
Send Your rain, send Your rain
      A   G   D
Send Your rain, send Your rain.

Ending:
A7sus2 D Dsus4 D
Send Your rain,
A7sus2 D Dsus4 D
Send Your rain,
A7sus2 D Dsus4 D
Send Your rain.

Taken from
BECAUSE OF YOUR LOVE
Brenton Brown
SURCD5124

SHE IS THERE IN THE CROWD ALONE

She's already gone

Tré Sheppard

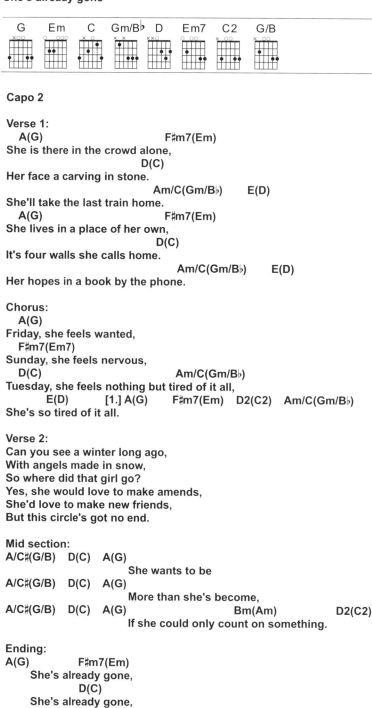

G   Em   C   Gm/B♭   D   Em7   C2   G/B

Capo 2

Verse 1:
```
 A(G)                      F♯m7(Em)
She is there in the crowd alone,
                  D(C)
Her face a carving in stone.
                   Am/C(Gm/B♭)      E(D)
She'll take the last train home.
 A(G)                      F♯m7(Em)
She lives in a place of her own,
                 D(C)
It's four walls she calls home.
                   Am/C(Gm/B♭)     E(D)
Her hopes in a book by the phone.
```

Chorus:
```
 A(G)
Friday, she feels wanted,
  F♯m7(Em7)
Sunday, she feels nervous,
 D(C)                     Am/C(Gm/B♭)
Tuesday, she feels nothing but tired of it all,
       E(D)      [1.] A(G)    F♯m7(Em)  D2(C2)  Am/C(Gm/B♭)
She's so tired of it all.
```

Verse 2:
Can you see a winter long ago,
With angels made in snow,
So where did that girl go?
Yes, she would love to make amends,
She'd love to make new friends,
But this circle's got no end.

Mid section:
```
A/C♯(G/B)   D(C)   A(G)
                     She wants to be
A/C♯(G/B)   D(C)   A(G)
                     More than she's become,
A/C♯(G/B)   D(C)   A(G)                 Bm(Am)          D2(C2)
                     If she could only count on something.
```

Ending:
```
A(G)         F♯m7(Em)
    She's already gone,
             D(C)
    She's already gone,
                 Bm(Am)          D2(C2)
    If she could only count on something.
```

Taken from
AS SURE AS THE STARS
Onehundredhours
SURCD5089

SING TO THE KING

(Come, let us sing a song)

Billy James Foote

1st verse & theme from 'Sing we the King' by Charles Silvester Horne (1865-1914)

E   B/E   A/E   F#m7   Asus2   Dsus2

Verse 1:

```
E          B/E        A/E          E
Sing to the King who is coming to reign;
         B/E       A/E        E
Glory to Jesus, the Lamb that was slain.
         B/E         A/E          E
Life and salvation His empire shall bring,
              B/E        A/E     E
And joy to the nations, when Jesus is King.
```

Chorus:

```
E
Come, let us sing a song,
    F#m7                          Asus2
A song declaring that we belong to Jesus;
A          E        Dsus2
He is all we need.
E
Lift up a heart of praise.
F#m7                           Asus2
Sing now with voices raised to Jesus;
             E
Sing to the King.
```

Verse 2:

```
For His returning we watch and we pray;
We will be ready the dawn of that day,
We'll join in singing with all the redeemed,
'Cause Satan is vanquished and Jesus is King.
```

Taken from
BEST OF PASSION
(so far)
SURCD5093

SING TO THE LORD

Nathan & Lou Fellingham
& busbee

98.

Verse 1:
```
         E                A/E        E
Sing to the Lord, give thanks for His greatness.
   A/E      E           A/E        E
Sing to the Lord, give thanks for His grace.
            D/A   A
His mercy is new today,
            D/A   A
Abounding in every way,
              E  F#m7/E  E
To all He has made.
```

Verse 2:
```
     A/E
Sing to the Lord,
Give thanks for His favour.
Sing to the Lord,
O people of God.
We're so precious in His sight,
He chose us before our life
Even began.
```

Chorus:
```
          B        C#m      A
Lift up your voice, and tell of His goodness,
        B        C#m      A
For He is perfect in all of His ways.
            B        C#m      D      A
Join in the song that is sung over all of the earth:
F#m7          B7sus4    E  Esus4  E
Lord, You're an amazing God.
```

Verse 3:
```
Sing to the Lord, give thanks for salvation.
Sing to the Lord, all you who are saved,
For once we were dead in sin,
But now we're alive in Him
And reigning with Christ.
```

Verse 4:
```
Sing to the Lord, give thanks for His kindness.
Sing to the Lord, O children of God.
The Spirit's available,
He'll help us prevail through all
That life throws our way.
```

Verse 5:
```
Sing to the Lord,
Give thanks for His power.
Sing to the Lord,
His kingdom is here.
Let's humble our hearts to Him,
Be ready to meet Him
As we call on His name.
```

Taken from
TREASURE
Lou Fellingham
KMCD2642

SO FEARFULLY AND WONDERFULLY MADE

(Fearfully and wonderfully made)

Matt & Beth Redman

Em   C   G   D   Gsus2 G/C Bm7 C2

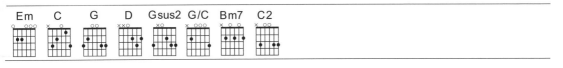

Capo 3

Verse 1:

    Em   C
So fearfully and wonderfully made,
             G   D
How could they say there is no God?
    Em   C
Reminded every breath that I take,
         G   D
It's by Your hand I have been formed.

Bridge

    C   D
So what am I going to do with this life You gave me,
C   D C
What could I do but live for Your praise?

Chorus:

    G   Gsus2   G/C
You gave me this breath,   and You gave me this strength,
    D   C
And every day I'll live to obey   You.
    G   Gsus2   G/C
With all of my heart,   with all of my soul,
    D   C   G
Let every breath I'm breathing display You, God. [Fine]

Verse 2:
There's elegance in all You create,
Your grand designs leave us amazed,
The wonders of the way we've been made,
Speak of Your power, tell of Your grace.

Mid section:
    D   C
So what am I going to do with this life You gave me?
D   C
What am I going to do with this life?
Bm7   C
What I am I going to do in these days You've ordained?
D   C2
What am I going to do with this life?

Taken from
BEAUTIFUL NEWS
Matt Redman
SURCD5071

(Fearfully and wonderfully made)

Matt & Beth Redman

Verse 1:

    Gm   E♭
So fearfully and wonderfully made,
               B♭   F
How could they say there is no God?
   Gm   E♭
Reminded every breath that I take,
        B♭   F
It's by Your hand I have been formed.

Bridge:
   E♭   F
So what am I going to do with this life You gave me,
E♭   F   E♭
What could I do but live for Your praise?

Chorus:
   B♭   B♭sus2   B♭/E♭
You gave me this breath,   and You gave me this strength,
   F   E♭
And every day I'll live to obey You.
  B♭   B♭sus2   B♭/E♭
With all of my heart,   with all of my soul,
   F   E♭   B♭
Let every breath I'm breathing display You, God. [Fine]

Verse 2:
There's elegance in all You create,
Your grand designs leave us amazed,
The wonders of the way we've been made,
Speak of Your power, tell of Your grace.

Mid section:
   F   E♭
So what am I going to do with this life You gave me?
F   E♭
What am I going to do with this life?
Dm7   E♭
What I am I going to do in these days You've ordained?
F   E♭2
What am I going to do with this life?

Taken from
BEAUTIFUL NEWS
Matt Redman
SURCD5071

STRENGTH WILL RISE

(Everlasting God)

Brenton Brown & Ken Riley

G   Gsus4   G/B   C   D   Em

Capo 3

Verse:
G   Gsus4   G
   Strength will rise as we wait upon the Lord,
     Gsus4   G   Gsus4   G
We will wait upon the Lord, we will wait upon the Lord. [Repeat]

G/B C
Our God,
G/B C   D Em D
You reign fore - ver.
G/B C
Our Hope,
G/B C   D Em D
Our strong deli - verer.

Chorus:
G   G/B C
   You are the everlasting God,
             Em
The everlasting God.
            C
You do not faint, You won't grow weary.
G   G/B C
   You're the defender of the weak,
              Em
You comfort those in need,
           C   G [G/B C   G/B C]
You lift us up on wings like eagles.   [Our God . . .]

Taken from
EVERLASTING GOD
Brenton Brown SURCD5031
UNIVERSAL
Yfriday SURCD5053
EMERGING CULTURE
SURCD5077

TAKE MY LIFE AND LET IT BE

Music: Paul Oakley

A   Em   G   D

Verse 1:
A   Em
  Take my life and let it be
G   D
  Consecrated, Lord, to Thee.
A   Em
  Take my moments and my days,
G   D
  Let them flow in ceaseless praise.
                   Em
  Take my hands and let them move
G   D
  At the impulse of Your love.
A   Em
  Take my feet and let them be
G   D
  Swift and beautiful for Thee.

Chorus:
D   G   Em
Oh, take my life, let it be
         D   A
Consecrated, Lord, to Thee.
              G   Em
Oh take my moments and my days,
        D   A   [Em G D A]
Let them flow   in ceaseless praise. [Last time D]

Verse 2:
Take my voice and let me sing
Always only for my King.
Take my lips and let them speak
Of the love that set me free.
Take my silver and my gold,
Not a mite would I withhold.
Take my intellect and use
Every gift as You shall choose.

Verse 3:
Take my will and let it bow,
You alone shall wear the crown.
Take my heart, make it Your own,
Let it be Your royal throne.
Take my love, my Lord, I pour
At Your feet its treasure store.
Take myself and I will be
Ever, only, all for Thee.

Frances R Havergal (1836-1879)
adpt. Paul Oakley

Taken from
FATHER ME
Paul Oakley
KMCD2728

TAKE MY LIFE

Frances Havergal (1836-79)
add. lyrics by Chris Tomlin & Louie Giglio

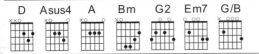

D Asus4 A Bm G2 Em7 G/B

Verse 1:

D   Asus4 A   Bm
  Take my life and let   it be
  G2   Em7   Asus4   D
Consecrated, Lord to Thee.
                  Asus4 A   Bm
Take my moments and   my days,
  G2   Em7   Asus4   A
Let them flow in ceasless praise.
C2   G/B
  Take my hands and let them move
Em7   Asus4   D
  At the impulse of Thy love.
                   Asus4 A Bm
Take my feet and let them   be
   G2   Em7 Asus4   D
Swift and beautiful for Thee.

Verse 2:
Take my voice, and let me sing
Always, only, for my King;
Take my lips, and let them be
Filled with messages from Thee.
Take my silver and my gold,
Not a mite would I withhold;
Take my intellect, and use
Every power as Thou shalt choose.

        Em7 G2   Asus4
Here am I,   all of me.
         Em7 G2   Asus4
Take my life,   it's all for Thee.

Verse 3:
Take my will, and make it Thine;
It shall be no longer mine:
Take my heart, it is Thine own;
It shall be Thy royal throne.
Take my love; my Lord, I pour
At Thy feet its treasure store:
Take myself, and I will be
Ever, only, all for Thee.

Frances Ridley Havergal (1836-79)

Taken from
THE BEST OF PASSION
(so far)
SURCD5093

THANK YOU, FATHER, FOR YOUR UNENDING GRACE   103.

(Keep me close)

Gareth Scott

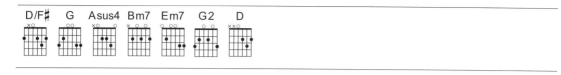

Capo 1

Verse 1:
D/F♯   G   Asus4 Bm7
Thank You, Fa - ther,
      G   Asus4
For Your unending grace.
D/F♯ G   Asus4 Bm7
You have saved me,
 G   Asus4
I come to You to praise.

Chorus:
Em7   D/F♯   G   Em7
   Without Your love, where would I be?
    D/F♯   G   Bm7
Without Your grace, where would I walk?
G   Asus4   Bm7
Keep me close to You,
G   Asus4   [D/F♯ G2   D/F♯   G2 x2] [Last time D]
Keep me close to You.

Verse 2:
You are holy,
Yet You reached out to us.
Through love You showed
Forgiveness at the cross.

Verse 3:
Thank You, Saviour,
For taking my sins place.
With arms wide You shouldered
The weight of all my shame.

Taken from
THE PEOPLE'S ALBUM, 3,
SURCD5140

THE DAY IS BRIGHTER
(Everything glorious)

David Crowder

C2   G   F6   F2   Am   G/B

Capo 1

Verse 1:
```
C2      G     F6           C2
   The day is brighter here with You,
        G     F6           C2
The night is lighter than it's hue,
         G   F6
Would lead me to believe,
C2          G     F6
   Which leads me to believe:
```

Chorus:
```
C           G         F2
You make everything glorious,
C           G         F2
You make everything glorious,
C           G         F2
You make everything glorious,
              C2  G   F2
And I am Yours,
                    C2  G   F2 [C2  G  F2]
What does that make me?
```

Verse 2:
My eyes are small, but they have seen
The beauty of enormous things,
Which leads me to believe
There's light enough to see that:

Mid section:
```
Am        G/B
   From glory to glory,
C                    G
   You are glorious, You are glorious.
F2        G/B
   From glory to glory,
C                  G
You are glorious, You are glorious.
F2
   Which leads me to believe
```

Why I can believe that.

Tag:
```
C        G  F2     C        G  F2
   From glory to glory, from glory to glory

C            G  F2
   You are glorious, You are glorious.
C            G  F2
   You are glorious, You are glorious.
```

Taken from
PASSION
Everything Glorious
SURCD5079

Copyright © 2005 worshiptogether.com songs/sixsteps Music. Adm by kingswaysongs.com
tym@kingsway.co.uk for the UK & Europe. Used by permission

(Everything glorious)

Verse 1:
D♭2   A♭   Gb♭   D♭2
   The day is brighter here with You,
      A♭   G♭6   DF2
The night is lighter than it's hue,
      A♭ G♭6
Would lead me to believe,
D♭2   A♭   G♭6
   Which leads me to believe:

Chorus:
D♭   A♭   G♭2
You make everything glorious,
D♭   A♭   G♭2
You make everything glorious,
D♭   A♭   G♭2
You make everything glorious,
           D♭2 A♭ G♭2
And I am Yours,
                D♭2 A♭ G♭2 [D♭2 A♭ G♭2]
What does that make me?

Verse 2:
My eyes are small, but they have seen
The beauty of enormous things,
Which leads me to believe
There's light enough to see that:

Mid section:
B♭m   A♭/C
   From glory to glory,
D♭   A♭
   You are glorious, You are glorious.
G♭2   A♭/C
   From glory to glory,
D♭   A♭
You are glorious, You are glorious.
G♭2
   Which leads me to believe

Why I can believe that.

Tag:
D♭   A♭ G♭2   D♭   A♭ G♭2
   From glory to glory, from glory to glory

D♭   A♭ G♭2
   You are glorious, You are glorious.
D♭   A♭ G♭2
   You are glorious, You are glorious.

Taken from
PASSION
Everything Glorious
SURCD5079

THE DISEASE OF MY SOUL

(Thank You for healing me)

G   Em7   C2   Am7   D   G2

Capo 4

Verse 1:
G   Em7
   The disease of my soul was spreading,
C2
Eating me up on the inside,
Am7
Keeping my heart from Your new life.
G   Em7
   And I see now where I was headed,
       C2
For there is no cure that can save us,
     Am7
Outside of Your mercy Lord Jesus.
D   C2
   Yes, You stepped in with Your power to save,
       D   C2
Let forgiveness reign, worked a miracle within.

Chorus:
                 G
Thank You for healing me,
      Em7
I was dying beneath my shame,
       D   C2
But You brought me to life again, and I will sing:
                 G
Thank You for freeing me,
       Em7
I was dead to the truth of You,
       D   C2
But my healing was in Your wounds, and now I sing:
                 [G2] [Last x G]
Thank You for healing me.   [Oh. To coda]

Mid section:
        D
Though outwardly I may waste away,
       C   G2
On the inside I'll be more alive every day.
     D
As I walk through times of pain and grief,
       C
There's a deeper truth inside of me,
          Em7
You have placed Your life inside of me, so I sing:

Coda:
G
   I'm alive, I'm alive,
Em7
   I'm alive, I'm alive in You.
D   C2
   Thank You for healing me. [Repeat]

Taken from
BEAUTIFUL NEWS
Matt Redman
SURCD5071

(Thank You for healing me)

Verse 1:
B   G♯m7
   The disease of my soul was spreading,
E2
Eating me up on the inside,
C♯m7
Keeping my heart from Your new life.
B   G♯m7
   And I see now where I was headed,
     E2
For there is no cure that can save us,
     C♯m7
Outside of Your mercy Lord Jesus.
F♯   E2
   Yes, You stepped in with Your power to save,
     F♯   E2
Let forgiveness reign, worked a miracle within.

Chorus:
          B
Thank You for healing me,
    G♯m7
I was dying beneath my shame,
      F♯   E2
But You brought me to life again, and I will sing:
          B
Thank You for freeing me,
     G♯m7
I was dead to the truth of You,
      F♯   E2
But my healing was in Your wounds, and now I sing:
         [B2] [Last x B]
Thank You for healing me.   [Oh. To coda]

Mid section:
     F♯
Though outwardly I may waste away,
     E   B2
On the inside I'll be more alive every day.
    F♯
As I walk through times of pain and grief,
      E
There's a deeper truth inside of me,
     G♯m7
You have placed Your life inside of me, so I sing:

Coda:
B
   I'm alive, I'm alive,
G♯m7
   I'm alive, I'm alive in You.
F♯   E2
   Thank You for healing me. [Repeat]

Taken from
BEAUTIFUL NEWS
Matt Redman
SURCD5071

THE GOD OF TIME AND ETERNITY

106.

Our God, He reigns

Simon Brading & Matt Redman

Bm   G   A   E   A/B

Capo 2

Verse 1:
```
    C#m(Bm)
```
The God of time and eternity
Orchestrates all history;
```
A(G)                      B(A)
```
Our God, He reigns forever.
```
    C#m(Bm)
```
At His command the whole world was made,
In His love, He came down to save;
```
A(G)                      B(A)
```
Our God, He reigns forever.
```
A(G)                      F#(E)
```
Our God, He reigns forever.

Chorus:
```
B(A)                 C#m(Bm)          A(G)
```
Our God, He reigns, our God, He reigns,
```
                  E(D)          B(A)
```
Now and forever, over all things.
```
                  C#m(Bm)          A(G)
```
The first and last word will always be His.
```
F#(E)      A(G)                    | C#m(Bm) | B/C#(A/B) C#m(Bm) | A(G) | B(A) |
```
Hallelujah, praise the God who reigns!

Verse 2:
The Father's plan of amazing grace,
Pierced hands for a sinful race;
Our God, He reigns forever.
And we exchange through His life and death
Guilty stains for His righteousness;
Our God, He reigns forever.
Our God, He reigns forever.

Verse 3:
He's seated high in authority
Yet lives inside of you and me;
Our God, He reigns forever.
Earthly power will fade away,
But Jesus' rule - it will never end;
Our God, He reigns forever.
Our God, He reigns forever.

End section:
```
A(G)   B(A)      F#(E)
```
Our   God reigns,
```
A(G)   B(A)      C#(B)
```
Our God reigns,
```
A(G)   B(A)      F#(E)
```
Our   God reigns,
```
A(G)        B(A)                   C#m(Bm)
```
Hallelujah, praise the God who reigns!

Taken from
LET THE RAIN COME
Newday Live
SURCD5116

THE LORD IS KING

(You're alive)

Chris Sayburn

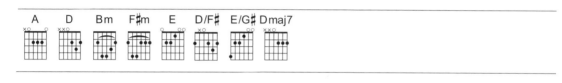

A   D   Bm   F#m   E   D/F#   E/G#   Dmaj7

Verse 1:

A
The Lord is King, robed in majesty;
                                                        D
Armed with strength, He rules over everything:
Bm   N.C.
   What an awesome God.
     A
Before His throne, elders bow the knee,
                                              D
Angels sing in glorious harmony:
Bm
   'Worthy is the Lord'.

Chorus:

          A
You're alive, You're alive, we worship You.
          F#m   E
You're alive, You're alive, we'll tell of Your great glory,
                        D
We're living for Your glory.
          A
Every day, every way, we worship You.
          F#m   E
What we do, what we say we'll tell of Your great glory,
                        D   [3. E] [Last x Dmaj7]
We're living for Your glory.

Verse 2:
Let all the earth revere His holy Name.
Three in One, victorious always:
What an awesome God.
Every knee will bow down at His feet,
Every tongue declare that He is King:
Jesus is King!

Mid section:
[E] D   E   D/F#   E/G#
For Yours is the kingdom, Yours is the power,
D   E   D/F#   E/G#   N.C.
Yours is the glory for ever and ever. [Repeat]

ever, amen!

Taken from
THE PEOPLE'S ALBUM, 3,
SURCD5140

THE LORD IS OUR ROCK

108.
Andy Ferrett
& Simon Brading

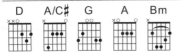

D   A/C♯   G   A   Bm

Verse 1:
```
D                    A/C♯        G
   The Lord is our rock,     able to save us;
                  A
Your word never fails.
D                    A/C♯     G
   You answer our call, King of salvation;
                A       G
We lift up our voice to You.
```

Chorus:
```
     D             A/C♯           Bm
Our God, You're greatly to be praised,
     G        D
You're gloriously worthy.
   A/C♯             Bm
We will lift up Your name
```

```
[1,2,4,5]  G             D
And shout about Your mercy.
```

```
[3,6]      G         Bm
And shout about Your mercy.
   A/C♯            G    [Bm   A/C♯   G x2  (D to end)]
And sing about Your mercy.
```

Verse 2:
King of the lost, Lord of the broken,
You know every thought.
You laugh with the joyful and cry with the hurting;
We lift up our voice to You.

THERE AT THE CROSS

Nick Herbert & John Peters

G D D/F♯ C G/F♯ Em

Capo 4(G)

Verse 1:
B(G)
There at the cross, I see Your glory,
                                F♯(D)
Still full of beauty, even in shame.
    B(G)   F♯/A♯(D/F♯)   E(C)   B(G)
The mystery of grace,   unending mercy,
E(C)   B(G)   F♯(D)
Revealed in weakness, made known in pain.

Chorus:
              B(G)   F♯/A♯(D/F♯)   E(C)   B(G)
You're the One   that I love:
E(C) B(G)   E(C) F♯(D)
Je - sus,   Je - sus.
              B(G)   F♯/A♯(D/F♯)   E(C)   B(G)
You're the One   I adore.
E(C) B(G)   E(C) F♯(D)   [1.] B(G) E(C) B/A♯(G/F♯) E(C)
Sa - viour,   Sa - viour.   [2.] to Mid Section
                                [3.] B(G)

Verse 2:
Before all time, worshipped in wonder,
Praise of creation and heaven above.
I gaze in awe at Your surrender,
Made Yourself nothing there at the cross.

Mid section:
G♯m(Em)   E(C)   B(G)
   I see You glorified in the sacrifice.
G♯m(Em)   E(C)   F♯(D)
   The greatest act of love is laying down Your life.
G♯m(Em)   E(C)   B(G)
   I see You glorified in the sacrifice.
G♯m(Em)   E(C)   F♯(D)
   The greatest act of love is laying down Your life.

THERE IS A CRIMSON STREAM

Paul Oakley

Crimson stream

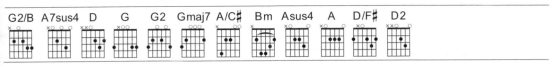

G2/B A7sus4 D G G2 Gmaj7 A/C# Bm Asus4 A D/F# D2

Capo 2

Verse 1:

  A2/C#(G2/B) B7sus4(A7sus4) E(D)
There is a   crimson   stream
 A(G) E(D) A2(G2)
That washes white as snow,
 A2/C#(G2/B) B/D#(A/C#) C#m(Bm) A(G) Bsus4(Asus4)
A love that longs to know me as Your own.
 A2/C#(G2/B) B7sus4(A7sus4) E(D)
This hope, the Light of   life,
 A(G) E(D) A2(G2)
This grace that won't let go,
 A2/C#(G2/B) B/D#(A/C#) C#m(Bm) A(G) Bsus4(Asus4)
This fire that burns can change a heart of stone.

Chorus:

A2(G2)   E(D)   Bsus4(Asus4)
 And nothing can stop this love from reaching me.
A2(G2)   E(D)   A(G) E(D) A2(G2)
 Nothing can keep Your blood from cleansing me.
A(G)   E(D)   A(G) E(D) A2(G2)
 Nothing can change Your mercies, new each day.
  B(A) C#m(Bm)
Oh, I believe in You.
 A(G) E/G#(D/F#) B7sus4(A7sus4) [to instr. fill]
My Jesus, I will give my heart to You.

Instrumental fill:

A2/C#(G2/B) E/G#(D/F#) A2/C#(G2/B) E/G#(D/F#)
A2/C#(G2/B) E/G#(D/F#) Bsus4(Asus4) [Last time:] E2(D2)

Verse 2:
No shame can keep me bound,
No sin can own the keys;
The price was paid in full to set me free.
No more these filthy rags;
I'm clothed in purity.
My Saviour's righteousness is mine to keep.

Taken from
LET THE RAIN COME
Newday Live
SURCD5109

THERE IS AN ENDLESS SONG

(How can I keep from singing)

Traditional, adpt. by Chris Tomlin, Matt Redman & Ed Cash

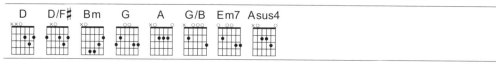

D   D/F♯   Bm   G   A   G/B   Em7 Asus4

Capo 3

Verse 1:
```
        D
There is an endless song,
        D/F♯
Echoes in my soul,
 Bm D/F♯ D Bm G
I hear the music   ring.
                D
And though the  storms may come,
      D/F♯
I am holding on,
Bm D/F♯  D Bm G
To  the Rock I   cling.
```

Chorus:
```
D                             A
How can I keep from singing Your praise,
        G           G/B
How can I ever say enough,
      G         A
How amazing is Your love?
D                             A
How can I keep from shouting Your name?
            G           D/F♯
I know I am loved by the King,
      G     A           D
And it makes my heart want to sing.
```

Verse 2:
```
I will lift my eyes
In the darkest night,
For I know my Saviour lives.
And I will walk with You,
Knowing You see me through,
And sing the songs You give.
```
```
    Em7        G/B        G         A
I can sing in the troubled times, sing when I win,
      Em7       D/F♯        G         D
I can sing when I lose my step, and I fall down again.
      Em7           G/B        G              A
I can sing 'cause You pick me up, sing 'cause You're there,
      Em7            G/B            G              A
I can sing 'cause You hear me, Lord, when I call to You in prayer.
      Em7       G/B     G       A
I can sing with my last breath, sing for I know
        Em7        G/B        G                Asus4   A
That I'll sing with the angels and the saints around the throne.
```

Inspired by the Robert Lowry hymn 'How can I keep from singing', c. 1860.

Taken from
SEE THE MORNING
Chris Tomlin
SURCD5084

THERE IS AN ENDLESS SONG

(How can I keep from singing)

Traditional, adpt. by Chris Tomlin,
Matt Redman & Ed Cash

Verse 1:
```
          F
There is an endless song,
       C/E
Echoes in my soul,
 Dm  C/E F  Dm  Bb
I hear the music    ring.
                    F
And though the  storms may come,
        C/E
I am holding on,
Dm C/E  F  Dm  Bb
To  the Rock I   cling.
```

Chorus:
```
F                            C
How can I keep from singing Your praise,
         Bb          C/E
How can I ever say enough,
      Bb         C
How amazing is Your love?
F                            C
How can I keep from shouting Your name?
           Bb         F/A
I know I am loved by the King,
      Bb        C          F
And it makes my heart want to sing.
```

Verse 2:
```
I will lift my eyes
In the darkest night,
For I know my Saviour lives.
And I will walk with You,
Knowing You see me through,
And sing the songs You give.
```

```
     Gm7       F/A        Bb         C
I can sing in the troubled times, sing when I win,
     Gm7       F/A          Bb         F
I can sing when I lose my step, and I fall down again.
     Gm7         F/A        Bb            C
I can sing  'cause You pick me up, sing 'cause You're there,
     Gm7          F/A            Bb          C
I can sing 'cause You hear me, Lord, when I call to You in prayer.
     Gm7         F/A        Bb      C
I can sing with my last breath, sing for I know
     Gm7       F/A        Bb         Csus4   C
That I'll sing with the angels and the saints around the throne.
```

Inspired by the Robert Lowry hymn 'How can I keep from singing', c. 1860.

Taken from
SEE THE MORNING
Chris Tomlin
SURCD5084

THERE'S A DARKNESS SOMETIMES

Safe in Your hands

Tré & Tori Sheppard, Mark Prentice,
Paul Baker, Jonny Ravn & Steve Evans

Am   Em   D   C   Fmaj7   C/G   Am7

Verse 1:
Am(Bm)*   Em(F#m)   D(E)
  There's a darkness sometimes,
Am(Bm)   Em(F#m)   D(E)
  Deeper than night,   yeah.
Am(Bm)   Em(F#m)   D(E)
Though I'm broken inside,
Am(Bm)   Em(F#m)   D(E)
I will reach for the Light.

Chorus:
C(D)
  This is all that I know,
Fmaj(Gmaj7)
  In this darkness below
C/G(D/A)   Am7(Bm7)
  Of heartache and plans,
C(D)
  Is that You carry my hope,
Fmaj(Gmaj7)
  And You light my way home;
C/G(D/A)   Am7(Bm7)
  I'm safe in Your hands.

Link [1st time only]:
Am(Bm)   Em(F#m) D(E)
Am(Bm)   Em(F#m) D(E)

Verse 2:
There's a place I can hide,
In Your love and Your light, yeah.
And the peace that I find,
It leads me to life.

Last chorus:
Jesus, all that I know,
In this darkness below
Of heartache and plans,
Is that You carry my hope,
And You light my way home;
I'm safe in Your hands.

Alternative chords for the song's original key.

Taken from
AS SURE AS THE STARS
Onehundredhours
SURCD5089

THERE'S A FIRE THAT RAGES

Rhythms of fire

Terl Bryant & Tim Hughes

Fsus2 Am Amsus2 C   F

Verse 1:
Fsus2
   There's a fire that rages
All across the land.
                                 Am Amsus2 Am Amsus2 Am
Tongues of fire falling down.
Fsus2
    All who see are humbled;
Reverently they bow,
                          C
Filled with faith receiving power.

Chorus:
              F
Rhythms of fire,
Rhythms of fire,
Rhythms of fire,
          Am Amsus2 Am
Falling down.
              F
Rhythms of fire,
Rhythms of fire,
Rhythms of fire,
         C
Falling down.

Verse 2:
Can you see the fire,
Feel the healing flames?
Your Kingdom come, Your will done.
Overwhelming, all consuming;
Nothing can withstand the place..
The final victory's come through Your flames

Taken from
RHYTHMS OF FIRE
Psalm Drummers
OVCD004

THERE'S A SONG THAT'S RISING UP

(Celebrate)

Ben Cantelon

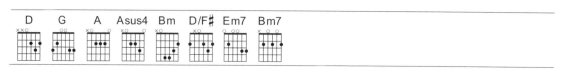

D G A Asus4 Bm D/F# Em7 Bm7

Verse 1:
       D   G   A   D
There's a song that's rising up inside,
         G   Asus4   A
It's the overflow of praise.
      Bm   A   G   D/F#
Your joy   has filled   this heart again,
     Em7   Bm7   A
No, I   am not the same.
                Em   Bm   Asus4   A
You have turned   sorrow into praise.

Chorus:
         D   G   Bm   A
We celebrate,   You've put dancing in our hearts.
         D   G   Bm   A
We celebrate   for all You've done and who You are.
           D/F# G   Bm   Asus4
We lift Your name   high above all other names.
           D/F# G   Asus4   A
You are Lord of heaven and earth.

Verse 2:
For the battle has already been won,
Even death You overcame.
We crown You King of glory now.
You reign victoriously;
We declare Your majesty.

        D/F#   G   Bm   A
I'll dance, I'll sing, giving glory to the King.
        D/F#   G   A
I'll praise Your name, for You reign.
          D/F#   G   Bm   A
We'll dance, we'll sing, giving glory to the King.
          D/F#   G   A
We'll praise Your name, for You reign.

Taken from
LOVE CAME DOWN
Soul Survivor Live 2006
SURCD5076
and
DAYLIGHT BREAKS THROUGH
Ben Cantelon
SURCD5094

THERE'S A WAR GOING ON

115.

(Come to the water)

Paul Baloche, Steven Curtis-Chapman, Stuart Garrard,Israel Houghton,
Tim Hughes, Graham Kendrick, Andy Park, Matt Redman,
Martin Smith, Michael W. Smith, Chris Tomlin, Darlene Zschech

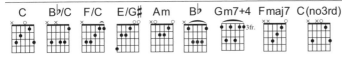

C   B♭/C   F/C   E/G♯   Am   B♭   Gm7+4   Fmaj7   C(no3rd)

Verse 1:

      C
There's a war going on just across the street,

There's a rage that's burning to an angry beat;
B♭/C   F/C
I can feel the thirst but there's no relief:
           C
We need a river.

There's a sound in the distance like a thunder cloud,

We're waiting for the rain while the sun beats down;
B♭/C   F/C
Can You feel is rising from the underground?
           C
We need a river.

Bridge:
E/G♯   Am
Oh, let justice roll like rivers,
E/G♯   Am   B♭
Oh, let mercy flow with love, love.

Chorus:
C
Come to the water,
Gm7+4   Fmaj7
Come to the water of life,

It will never run dry.
C
Come to the water,
Gm7+4   Fmaj7
Run to the water of life,
                    C(no3rd)
It will never run dry.

2.
There's a cry form the child in the factory,
There's a prayer for the prisoners of poverty:
Save us from the greed and the apathy –
We need a river.
There's a hope like a river running dowwn our street,
We're an army of peacemakers on our feet:
Take us top the place love and mercy meet –
There is a river.

Taken from
COMPASSIONART

THERE'S NO ONE, THERE'S NO ONE LIKE JESUS 116.

Trad. Author unknown

G   C   D   G/D

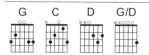

      G   C
There's no one, there's no one like Jesus,
      G   D
There's no one, there's no one like Jesus.
      G   C
There's no one, there's no one like Jesus,
    G/D   D   G
There's no one, there's no one like Him.

   G   C
I walk, I walk here and there.
   G   D
I search and search here and there.
   G   C
I turn around here and there.
      G/D   D   G
There's no one, there's no one like Him.

   G   C
Akekho ofana no Yesus.
   G   D
Akekho ofana no Yesus.
    G   C
Akekho ofana no Yesus.
  G/D   D   G
Akekho ofana naye.

   G   C
Ndiahamba hamba phaya phaya.
   G   D
Ndiyafuna funa phaya phaya.
   G   C
Ndiyajika jika phaya phaya.
  G/D   D   G
Akekho ofana naye.

Taken from
SHOUT FROM THE ROOF
Newday 2006
SURCD5075

THE STARS ARE SINGING OF OUR GOD

Stars

Brenton Brown

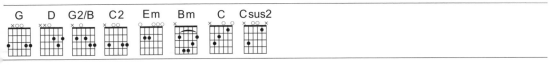

G   D   G2/B   C2   Em   Bm   C   Csus2

Capo 2(G)

Verse 1:
    A(G)   E(D)   A2/C♯(G2/B)   D2(C2)
The stars are singing of our God,
    A(G)   E(D)   A2/C♯(G2/B)   D2(C2)
The mountains tell how great You are,
    A(G) E(D)   A2/C♯(G2/B)   D2(C2)
The ocean speaks of Your endless power;
                 F♯m(Em)
And everyone should know it,
E(D)   C♯m(Bm)   D(C)
   Everyone should know it's true.
              F♯m(Em)
Everyone should know it,
E(D)   C♯m(Bm)   D(C)
   Everyone should know it's true.

Verse 2:
You chose to leave Your father's side
With all Your glory left behind.
You showed us how to live this life.
And everyone should know it,
Everyone should know it's true.
Everyone should know it,
E(D)   C♯m(Bm) Dsus2(Csus2)
   Everyone should know that You are

Chorus:
       A(G)   E(D)
Awesome God, strong and mighty.
      F♯m(Em)   D(C)
Maker of - the universe.
      A(G)   E(D)
High above, yet in Your mercy
      F♯m(Em)   D(C)
You reached down - and rescued us.
            Dsus2(Csus2)
You remembered us.

Verse 3:
The cross reveals the heart of God;
Our Maker, crucified for us.
You chose to be our sacrifice
And everyone should know it,
Everyone should know it's true.
Everyone should know it,
Everyone should know that You are

Taken from
BECAUSE OF YOUR LOVE
Brenton Brown
SURCD5124

THE WORLD IS NOT ENOUGH

(Take the world)

Tim Hughes

G   D   Em7   C2

Capo 1

```
     G          D       Em7     C2
The world is not enough for me.
     G          D       Em7     C2
The world is not enough for me.
       G         D       Em7      C2     G   D  Em7  C2
The world is not enough for me, yeah. [Repeat]
                         G    D   Em7   C2
It's not enough for me.


G            D              Em7      C2
   You can take the world,     just give me You.
G            D              Em7       C2        G   D  Em7  C2
   You can take the world,     just give me You,          yeah.


Last time:
G            D              Em7      C2         G   D   Em7  C2 [G]
   You can take the world,     all I want is You.
```

Taken from
HOLDING NOTHIN
BACK Tim Hughes
SURCD5068

Because of Your love

Al Gordon & Hanif Williams

G   Em   C   D   A   A/E

Capo 4

Verse 1:
B(G)
   This is how I know what love is, this is how I know I'm free,
This is how I know salvation: Jesus came and died for me.
This is why I come to worship, this is why I lift my hands,
G♯m(Em)
   This is why I now surrender
B(G)
   Everything I am:

Chorus:
          E(C)   B(G)
Because of Your love;
      G♯m(Em)   F♯(D)
There's dancing in my heart.
          E(C)   B(G)
Because of Your grace
     C♯(A)   C♯/G♯(A/E)
I am free.
          E(C)   B(G)
Because of Your faithfulness
       G♯m(Em)   F♯(D)
There's a song that must be sung,
      E(C)   B(G)   F♯(D)   [1st time only:] B(G)
And I will sing, I will sing because of You

Verse 2:
B(G)
   This is why there's joy within me, this is why my spirit sings:
G♯m(Em)   E(C)
   Jesus, You're my great adventure;
B(G)
   You're my everything.

Mid section:
    E(C)   F♯(D)   G♯m(Em)
You came to save the world,
    B(G)   E(C) B(G)   F♯(D)
To save the world, to save the world.
    E(C)   F♯(D)   G♯m(Em)
Your love can change the world,
    B(G)   E(C)   B(G)   F♯(D)
Can change the world, can change the world.

Ending:
     E(C)   B(G)
I will dance, I will dance
           F♯(D)
Because of You.
      E(C)
I will dance
B(G)   F♯(D)
   Because of You.

Taken from
FUTURE SOUND
Al Gordon
SURCD5125

WE ARE THIRSTY FOR YOU

Let the rain come

Simon Brading, Kate Simmonds
& Ben Hall

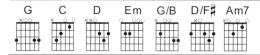

G C D Em G/B D/F♯ Am7

Capo 3

Verse 1:
```
         B♭(G)         E♭(C)    F(D)      B♭(G)
We are thirsty for You to flood our lives,
         B♭(G)         E♭(C)  F(D)
We are thirsty for You today.
         B♭(G)         E♭(C)    F(D)       Gm(Em)
We are thirsty to see and savour Christ;
     B♭/D(G/B)      E♭(C)    F(D)
Lord, send Your revival rain.
```

Bridge:
```
        Gm(Em)      E♭(C)
Let it rain, let it rain.
B♭/D(G/B)       E♭(C)            F(D)
Open up the heavens once again.
```

Chorus:
```
B♭(G)         F/A(D/F♯)
  Our Father    in heaven,
Cm7(Am7)      E♭(C)
Send the rain, fall again on us.
B♭(G)                 F/A(D/F♯)
  For Your kingdom,    Your glory,
Cm7(Am7)
Send the rain,
E♭(C)                                      [1.] B♭(G)  F(D)  Cm7(Am7)  E♭(C)
Let the rain come, let the rain come on us. [2.] Gm(Em)  F/A(D/F♯)  B♭(G)  Cm7(Am7)
                                           [3.] B♭(G)
```

Verse 2:
```
Holy Spirit, the more we see of Christ,
We'll have passion to make Him known.
Then the whole world might know that You are God:
Lord, send Your revival rain.
```

Mid section:
```
Gm(Em)
Let the rain come, let the rain come,
F/A(D/F♯)
Let the rain come, let the rain come,
B♭(G)                       Cm7(Am7)
Let the rain come, let the rain come on us.  [Repeat]
```

Taken from
LET THE RAIN COME
Newday Live
SURCD5117

WE BOW OUR HEARTS

(Adoration)

Brenton Brown

Verse 1:
```
   G                  D
We bow our hearts, we lift our hands,
   Em7           C
We turn our eyes to You again,
   G             D
And we surrender to the truth
   Em7              C
That all we need is found in You.
```

Chorus:
```
           G      D       Em       Em7  C
Receive our adoration, Jesus, Lamb of God.
           G      D         Em    Em7  C
Receive our adoration; how wonderful You are.
```

Verse 2:
We choose to leave it all behind
And turn our eyes towards the prize.
The upward call of God in Christ;
You have our hearts, Lord; take our lives.

Mid section:
```
              D     Dsus4 D
Every soul You've saved sings   out.
              C      G
Everything You've made resounds.
           D     Dsus4 D
All creation's standing      now,
       C
Lifting up Your name.
                 D Dsus4  D
We're caught up in the angel's    song.
                 C      G
We're gathered to Your ancient throne.
           D Dsus4  D
Children in our Father's   arms,
       C
Shouting out Your praise.
```

Taken from
BECAUSE OF YOUR LOVE
Brenton Brown
SURCD5124

WE CAN HEAR IT GROWING LOUDER

122.

(Amazing God)

Brenton Brown

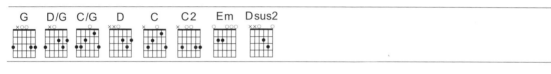

Verse 1:
G   D/G
We can hear it growing louder;
                  C/G
Songs from every nation rising to Your throne.
G   D/G
Saints in every generation
                C/G
Singing for Your glory, telling what You've done.

Bridge:
        D   C
From the north and south, we are crying out:
        D   C
There is hope in Jesus' name.

Chorus:
                      G   C2
'Cause You're amazing God, You're amazing God.
                 Em   Dsus2   C2
You can bear the weight of every heavy heart.
                      G   C2
You can heal the pain, You can clean the stain.
                 Em   Dsus2   C2
You can turn our tears into songs of praise.
                      G
You're amazing God.

Verse 2:
Beauty rises from the ashes,
Sorrow turns to gladness
When our God is near.
You speak light into our darkness,
You heal the broken-hearted,
You wipe away our tears.

Mid section:
| G | G | C | C | Em | D | C |
C   G
Songs of praise surround us,
                 C
Songs of praise surround us.
              Em
Hear it growing louder,
D   C2
We are growing louder.

[Last time:]
C   Em D C
We are growing loud - er.

Taken from
BECAUSE OF YOUR LOVE
Brenton Brown
SURCD5124

WE COULD TRY

(King of wonder)

123.

Paul Baloche, Steven Curtis-Chapman, Stuart Garrard,Israel Houghton,
Tim Hughes, Graham Kendrick, Andy Park, Matt Redman,
Martin Smith, Michael W. Smith, Chris Tomlin, Darlene Zschech

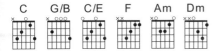

C G/B C/E F Am Dm

Verse 1:
```
C                G/B
We could try to count the stars;
   C/E       F              C  G/B  C/E  F
You already know them each by name.
Am           G/B
Every single galaxy
   C/E          F            Am  G/B  C/E  F
Is Your design In majesty displayed.
```

Bridge:
```
          Dm            C
Your glory shines before our eyes;
          F           Am  G
The more we see, the more we love   You.
```

Chorus:
```
C
King of wonders, we stand amazed,
F
There's no other, other than You.
Am                                  F
King of wonders, You know the way to our hearts,
                         [Am   C/E   F  last time x2]
And the more we see, the more we love You.
```

Verse 2:
```
You reveal and we respond –
You have shown there's no one like You God;
Your love and mercy welcome us
Into the beauty of this holiness.
```

Taken from
COMPASSIONART

WE HAVE SEEN ALL YOUR GOODNESS

(And we wait for You)

Andy Ferrett

Verse 1:

           A2   E
We have seen   all Your goodness,
     D2   A2
From afar   and in our lives.
               A2   E
We've been touched   by Your mercy,
            D2   A
Known Your grace   and Your forgiveness.

Chorus:

              E   F#m7
And so we wait for You to come;
     E   A
So we call upon Your endless love.
     E   F#m7
So we long for You to fall,
     E   A
Like a flood, Lord, let Your glory come.

Verse 2:
We have stood in Your river,
Drunk Your wine and tasted Your word.
You have poured Your Spirit upon us,
All Your blessings showered on us.

WE NEED YOU, HOW WE NEED YOU

Brenton Brown

Inspired by 'I need thee every hour' by Annie Hawks, 1872

D   A   Bm   G   Dsus4   Asus4   Em7   G2

Verse 1:
D
We need You, how we need You,
  A
We need You every hour;
  Bm
To see You in Your glory,
  G
To know Your Spirit's power.
     D
There's healing in Your presence,
    A
There's mercy where You are.
  Bm   G   A   D   Dsus4 D
So meet us, won't You meet us, living God.

Chorus:
        G   D
No other God but You,
        G   A   Bm
No other God but You,
        G   D   A   Asus4 A
No other God can satisfy.
          G   D
You are our great reward,
              G   A   Bm
It's You we're longing for.
        G   D   A   Asus4 A   [Last time:] G2 G D
No other God but You, most high.

Verse 2:
Each trial and each temptation,
Each enemy we fear
Retreats in resignation
When the living God is near.
So we kneel again before You,
O keeper of our hearts,
And we ask for Your deliverance,
Living God.

Verse 3:
One day we'll stand before You,
When all our sufferings cease,
And faced with all Your glory,
We'll meet the Prince of peace.
But Jesus, in that moment,
When every trial has passed,
We will need You, still we'll need You,
Living God.

Mid section:
       G   D   A   Em7
We are leaning on Your everlasting arms.
       G   D   Asus4   A
Lord, we know You'll see us through.
       G D   A   Em7
Great redeemer, be the song within our hearts.
          G   D   A
We'll have no other God but You.

Taken from
BECAUSE OF YOUR LOVE
Brenton Brown
SURCD5124

WE REJOICE

(Siyavuya kuwe)

Evan Rogers

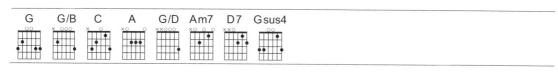

G   G/B   C   A   G/D Am7   D7 Gsus4

Verse 1:
```
     G                  G/B      C
We rejoice because You came from heav'n to earth,
     G/B                   C
Laying down Your majesty in humble birth.
   A                        C
We rejoice because You have so loved the world;
      G/D          D  G  Gsus4   G
You are Christ, Emmanuel.
```

Verse 2:
```
                      G/B    C
We rejoice because You lived a perfect life;
        G/D        G/B  C
With our frailty You have identified.
   A                        C
We rejoice because You came to make us whole.
      G/D          D   G  Gsus4   G
You're the shepherd of our souls.
```

Chorus:
```
        C G
Siyavuya kuwe.
        C G
Siya vuya kuwe.
      C G/D
Siyavuya kuwe.
      Am7        D7 G  [Gsus4   G]
Jesu A kekho fan' nawe.
```

English chorus:
```
G          C G
We rejoice in You.
            C G
We rejoice in You.
          C G/D
We rejoice in You.
      Am7          D7 G   [Gsus4   G]
Jesus there is none like You.
```

Verse 3:
We are humbled that Your life led to the cross;
There You gave Yourself, a sacrifice for us.
We are humbled at the way You suffered pain,
Lamb of God for sinners slain.

Verse 4:
I rejoice because You have forgiven my sin;
You received the Father's wrath - my punishment.
I rejoice because of Your amazing grace;
Now I'm free from guilt and shame.

Verse 5:
We rejoice because You broke the curse of death;
Now we live in hope, sure of eternal rest.
We rejoice because You've made our home in heaven,
Where we'll worship You forever.

Verse 6:
We rejoice because You sit at God's right hand
And before Your throne we're lifting up Your name.
We'll rejoice when every tribe and tongue proclaims
'Jesus is the Lord who reigns!'

Taken from
SHOUT FROM THE ROOF
Newday 2006
SURCD5075

WE WILL SING, SING, SING

Sing, sing, sing

Chris Tomlin, Jesse Reeves,
Matt Gilder & Daniel Carson

127.

D(no3rd) Bm7 Asus4 G(no3rd) D Csus2 Gsus2

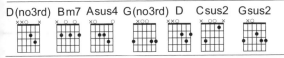

Chorus:
      D(no3rd)
(We will) sing, sing, sing
And make music with the heavens.
      Bm7
We will sing, sing, sing,
Grateful that You hear us
        Asus4
When we shout Your praise,
  G(no3rd)   D(no3rd)
Lift high the name of Jesus.

Verse 1:
D(no3rd)
  What's not to love about You?
  Heaven and earth adore You.
Bm7
  Kings and kingdoms bow down.
              Asus4
  Son of God, You are the One,
       G(no3rd)   D
You are the One we're living for.

Verse 2:
You are the love that frees us.
You are the light that leads us,
Like a fire burning.
Son of God, You are the One,
You are the One.

Mid section:
| Csus2 | Csus2 | Gsus2 | Gsus2 | Gsus2 | Gsus2 | D | D | D | D |

Taken from
GOD OF THIS CITY
Passion
SURCD5126

WE, YOUR CHILDREN PRAY

(King of the broken)

Paul Baloche, Steven Curtis-Chapman, Stuart Garrard,Israel Houghton,
Tim Hughes, Graham Kendrick, Andy Park, Matt Redman,
Martin Smith, Michael W. Smith, Chris Tomlin, Darlene Zschech

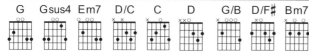

G   Gsus4 Em7   D/C   C   D   G/B   D/F♯   Bm7

Capo 1:

Verse 1:
```
G                    Gsus4 G
We, Your children, pray    Lord,
                     Gsus4   G
Humbly seek Your face;
Em7              D/C C
We turn from our sin,   Lord,
      G                    D
You hear the sounds we bring.
```

Verse 2:
Healing King of nations,
Let your kingdom come.
Purify your church, Lord,
Your Glory over us.

Bridge:
```
C           G/B
Heal us, forgive us,
    D                Em7
Restore our hearts again.
C      D
Fill us, breathe upon us.
```

Chorus:
```
Gsus4  G   D/F♯   Em7
Je  -  sus, Jesus, Healer of nations,
C
Hope of salvation.
Gsus4  G   Bm7   Em7
Je  -  sus, Jesus, King of our hearts,
C                  [1. G  Gsus4 G   Gsus4 G]
King of  the broken. [2. Am G     C   Em7   D   Am   G   C   D/C   C]
                     [Last time:    G]
```

Verse 3:
Lover of the wounded,
Defender of the weak,
Friend of the forgotten;
You wipe away our tears.

Taken from
COMPASSIONART

WHAT A BEAUTIFUL THING

129.

Say it with this song

Nick Herbert & John Peters

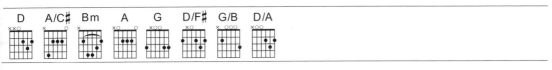

D A/C# Bm A G D/F# G/B D/A

Capo 2(D)

Verse 1:
E(D)   B/D#(A/C#)
  What a beautiful thing;
C#m(Bm)   B(A)
  Singing these songs to You, my King.
A(G)   E/G#(D/F#)
  Made to love You,
A/C#(G/B)   B(A)
  Made to love You.

Verse 2:
When the anthems of praise
Have been sung, still my heart will say:
My everything,
You are my everything.

Chorus 1:
     E/G#(D/F#)
Jesus, I love You.
A(G)   E/B(D/A)
  Jesus, I'll love You always.
A(G)   E/G#(D/F#)
  I'll say it with this song.
A/C#(G/B)   E/G#(D/F#) A(G)
  Jesus, I'll love You   always. Always.

Verse 3:
No good thing You withhold,
I'm dependent on You alone.
Reason I sing,
You're the reason I sing.

Chorus 2:
Spirit, I love.
Spirit, I'll love You always.
I'll say it with this song.
Spirit, I'll love You always.

Chorus 3:
     E/G#(D/F#)
Father, I love You.
A(G)   E/B(D/A)
  Father, I'll love You always.
A(G)   E/G#(D/F#)
  I'll say it with this song.
A/C#(G/B)   E/G#(D/F#)   A(G)
  Father, I'll love You always.
    E(D)
Always.

WHAT DOES IT MEAN TO BE A BIBLE MACHINE? 130.

(Let it glow)

Paul Baloche, Steven Curtis-Chapman, Stuart Garrard, Israel Houghton,
Tim Hughes, Graham Kendrick, Toby Mac, Andy Park, Matt Redman,
Martin Smith, Michael W. Smith, Chris Tomlin, Darlene Zschech

A(no3rd) G(no3rd) F#(no3rd) F(no3rd) C(no3rd)

Verse 1:
A(no3rd)   G(no3rd)
What does it mean to be a bible machine
   F#(no3rd)   F(no3rd)
In a planetary system that rotates without a dream?
   G(no3rd) A(no3rd)   G(no3rd)
I'm not a   number but a name, please excuse me all the same,
   F#(no3rd)   F(no3rd)   G(no3rd)
If I sing about love, truth and world that lives in pain: come on!

Chorus:
A(no3rd)
Oh,   oh,   oh,

Let it go, let it show, let it glow, you say.

Oh,   oh,   oh,

Let it go, let it show, let it glow, so sing.

Verse 2:
What does it mean to fill the pews on the weekend,
Ignoring the world that's dying just outside the door?
This little light of mine, I'm about to let it shine
This microphone is for the streets, not for V.I.P.'s in seats.

Bridge:
A(no3rd) //// //// //// //// C(no3rd) //// //// //// ////

A(no3rd)
  I got to let it flow, I got to let is show,

I got to let it go, I got to let it glow.
C(no3rd)
  We got to let it go, we got to let it show,

We got to let it, got to let it, got to let it glow.

Taken from
COMPASSIONART

WHAT GOOD IS IT?

(Living for Your glory)

Tim & Rachel Hughes

Am   C   F   Dm   G   F2

Capo 4

Verse 1:
Am   C
   What good is it to gain the whole world,
       F
But lose your soul?
Am   C
   What good is it to make a sweet sound,
      F
But remain proud?

Bridge:
Dm C   G F
   In view of God's mercy,
Dm C   G
   I offer my all.

Chorus:
      F2
And take my life, let it be
G   Am
Everything, all of me;
F2   G C
Here I am, use me for Your glory.
   F2
In everything I say and do,
G   Am
Let my life honour You,
F2   G C
Here I am, living for Your glory.

Verse 2:
The road I'm on, it leads nowhere
Without You,
And the life I lead, it finds meaning
In surrender.

F2   G   Am F2
   Seeking first the kingdom,
            G   Am G   F2
Seeking first the kingdom of   my Lord. [Repeat]

Taken from
HOLDING NOTHING BACK
Tim Hughes
SURCD5068

WHAT GOOD IS IT?

(Living for Your glory)

Tim & Rachel Hughes

Verse 1:
C#m   E
   What good is it to gain the whole world,
        A
But lose your soul?
C#m   E
   What good is it to make a sweet sound,
       A
But remain proud?

Bridge:
F#m E   B A
   In view of God's mercy,
F#m E   B
   I offer my all.

Chorus:
     A2
And take my life, let it be
B   C#m
Everything, all of me;
A2   B E
Here I am, use me for Your glory.
   A2
In everything I say and do,
B   C#m
Let my life honour You,
A2   B E
Here I am, living for Your glory.

Verse 2:
The road I'm on, it leads nowhere
Without You,
And the life I lead, it finds meaning
In surrender.

A2   B   C#m A2
   Seeking first the kingdom,
                B   C#m B   A2
Seeking first the kingdom of   my Lord. [Repeat]

Taken from
HOLDING NOTHING BACK
Tim Hughes
SURCD5068

WHEN ALL IS STRIPPED AWAY

(No one like You)

Ian Yates

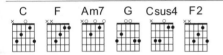

Verse 1:
```
C                        F
  When all is stripped away,
Am7                      F
  When brokenness abounds,
C                      F
  When all is confusing,
Am7                      F
  When weakness abounds;
G          F
  I find my rest in You,
G          F
  I find my hope in You.
```

Chorus:
```
       Csus4  C   F2
Jesus,         Jesus,
         Am7
There is no one like You,
             G
There is no one like  You.
       Csus4  C   F2
Jesus,           Jesus,
         Am7
There is no one like You,
       G              F        [C   F2   Am7   F2]
There is no one like You, [Jesus.] [Last x Csus4   C]
```

Verse 2:
When all falls away,
You carry me through.
Yet to stand in my failure,
You stood in my place.
I find forgiveness in You,
I find redemption in You.

Mid section:
```
   C
And there will be no other,
   F2
There will be no other,
     Am7                 F2
1. There will be no other but You. Jesus, there . . .
     Am7             F2     Csus4
2. There will be no other but You.   Jesus.   Jesus . . .
```

Taken from
THE PEOPLE'S ALBUM, 3,
SURCD5140

WHEN ALL SEEMS LOST

133.

Everlasting arms

Al Gordon

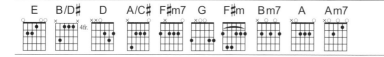

E B/D♯ D A/C♯ F♯m7 G F♯m Bm7 A Am7

Verse 1:
E   B/D♯
  When all seems lost
      D   A/C♯
And there's no song to sing.
E   B/D♯
I lean into the arms
      D   A/C♯
Of one who carries me.
      E   F♯m7
And if my world crumbles
         G   F♯m
And my heart feels ground to dust.

Chorus 1:
      E   Bm7
I'll still be in Your arms,
         A   Am7
Those everlasting arms.
      E   Bm7
I'm safe here in Your arms,
         A   Am7 (E B/D♯ D A/C♯)
Those everlasting arms.

Verse 2:
When sorrows come sweeping like a flood,
I'll cling onto the rock of Your unfailing love.
Father, hold me closer and still my beating heart.

Chorus 2:
Keep me in Your arms,
Those everlasting arms.
I'm safe here in Your arms,
Those everlasting arms.

Tag:
E   B/D♯
Leaning on Your arms,
      D   A/C♯
Those everlasting arms.
E   B/D♯
Safe here in Your arms,
      D   A/C♯
Those everlasting arms.   [Repeat]

Home in Your arms,
Those everlasting arms.
Safe here in Your arms,
Those everlasting arms.   [Repeat]

Instrumental Tag:
E   B/D♯   D   A/C♯
E   B/D♯   D   A/C♯   (E)

Taken from
FUTURE SOUND
Al Gordon
SURCD5125

WHEN CLOUDS VEIL SUN

Never let go

134.

Mike Hogan, David Crowder
& Mike Dodson

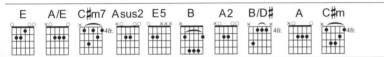

E   A/E   C#m7 Asus2 E5   B   A2   B/D#   A   C#m

Verse 1:
```
E                    A/E
  When clouds veil sun
E                    A/E
  And disaster comes,
          E          A/E
Oh, my soul, oh, my soul.
E                    A/E
  When waters rise
E                       A/E
  And hope takes flight,
         E           A/E
Oh, my soul, oh, my soul.
E              A/E
  Oh, my soul.
C#m7     Asus2
  Ever faithful, ever true.
E5         B                A2
  You, I know, You never let go.
```

Verse 2:
```
When clouds brought rain and disaster came,
Oh, my soul, oh, my soul.
When waters rose and hope had flown,
Oh, my soul, oh, my soul.
Oh, my soul.
Ever faithful, ever true.
You, I know, You never let go.
```

Chorus:
```
E              A2             E
  You never let go, You never let go,
              Asus2
You never let go.
E              A2             E
  You never let go, You never let go,
              Asus2  [1. E Asus2 E Asus2]
You never let go.
```

Mid Section:
```
B          Asus2      E5
  Oh, my soul overflows.
          B/D#           Asus2
Oh, what love, oh, what love.
          B              E5
Oh, my soul fills with hope,
          B/D#               Asus2
Perfect love that never lets go.
```

Ending:
```
|E|A|E|A|E|A|E|A|
C#m          A
  Oh, what love, oh, what love.
E            A
  Oh, what love. [X2]
C#m          A
  Joy and pain, in sun and rain,
E              A
  You're the same.  Oh, You never let go. [X3]
C#m          A          E
  Never let go, never let go.
```

Taken from
REMEDY
David Crowder Band
SURCD5101

WHEN I CALL ON YOUR NAME

(Love came down)

Ben Cantelon

G   C   Am7   G/B   Em7   D   Em

Capo 3

Verse 1:
```
          G                        C
When I call on Your name, You answer;
          G                        C
When I fall, You are there by my side.
          G                   C
You delivered me out of darkness,
            G                      C
Now I stand in the hope of new life.
```

Bridge:
```
        Am7       G/B      C
By grace I'm free, You've rescued me;
Am7     G/B    C
All I am is Yours.
```

Chorus:
```
G
    I've found a love greater than life itself.
C
    I've found a hope stronger and nothing compares.
Em7                              C
    I once was lost, now I'm alive in You.
```

Verse 2:
You're my God and my firm foundation;
It is You whom I'll trust at all times.
I give glory and praise, adoration
To my Saviour who's seated on high.

Mid section:
```
D                    Em
Love came down and rescued me.
C         G
  I thank You,    I thank You.
 D                    Em
I once was blind, but now I see.
C         G
  I see You,    I see You.
```

Taken from
LOVE CAME DOWN
Soul Survivor Live 2006
SURCD5076

WHEN I CALL ON YOUR NAME

(Love came down)

Ben Cantelon

Verse 1:

      B♭   E♭
When I call on Your name, You answer;
      B♭   E♭
When I fall, You are there by my side.
    B♭   E♭
You delivered me out of darkness,
       B♭   E♭
Now I stand in the hope of new life.

Bridge:

      Cm7   B♭/D   E♭
By grace I'm free, You've rescued me;
Cm7   B♭/D   E♭
All I am is Yours.

Chorus:

B♭
  I've found a love greater than life itself.
E♭
  I've found a hope stronger and nothing compares.
Gm7   E♭
  I once was lost, now I'm alive in You.

Verse 2:

You're my God and my firm foundation;
It is You whom I'll trust at all times.
I give glory and praise, adoration
To my Saviour who's seated on high.

Mid section:

F   Gm
Love came down and rescued me.
E♭   B♭
  I thank You,   I thank You.
 F   Gm
I once was blind, but now I see.
E♭   B♭
  I see You,   I see You.

Taken from
LOVE CAME DOWN
Soul Survivor Live 2006
SURCD5076

WHEN I NEED SOMEONE

Love, rescue me

Tré & Tori Sheppard
& Kathryn Scott

Em   C   G   D   G/B

Capo 5 (for original key)

Verse 1 & 3:
Em   C   G   D
When I need someone to quiet my fears,
        Em   C   G/B   D
Till the whispers inside me all disappear;
Em   C   G   D
When I need someone to dry all my tears,
 Em   C G D
I wait for You,
        Em   C G D
Yes, I wait for You.

Verse 2:
When I taste sorrow, when pain is my friend,
When I can't hide what's broken, I can't pretend;
When all that I hoped for has faded again,
I wait for You, yes, I'll wait for You.

Chorus:
Em   C   G   D
  Love, rescue me,
Em   C   G   D
  Love, rescue me.
Em   C   G   D
  Love, rescue me,
Em   C   G   D
  Love, rescue me.

Mid section:
D
  This longing,
C
  This aching,
G
  Only Your love can rescue me.
D
  I'm calling,
C
  Here waiting;
G   C
  Oh, send Your love to rescue me.

Taken from
AS SURE AS THE STARS
Onehundredhours
SURCD5089

WHEN I SURVEY

Chorus & Music: Tim Hughes
Verses: Isaac Watts (1674-1748)

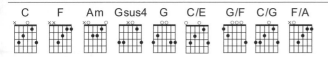

C   F   Am   Gsus4   G   C/E   G/F   C/G   F/A

Verse 1:
```
        C   F            C
When I survey   the wondrous cross
          Am    F        Gsus4
On which the Prince   of glory died,
G          C/E  F       Am
  My richest gain   I count but loss
Fmaj7         C     F    G    C   F  C/E   F
  And pour contempt    on all my pride.
```

Verse 2:
```
F         C    F              C
See from His head,   His hands, His feet,
          Am   F             Gsus4
Sorrow and love   flow mingled down.
G        G/F  C/E  F          Am
  Did e'er such love    and sorrow meet,
F            C    F    G    C    F  C/E   F
  Or thorns compose   so rich a crown?
```

Verse 3:
```
Were the whole realm of nature mine,
That were a offering far too small;
Love so ama zing, so divine,
Demands my soul, my life, my all.
```

Chorus:
```
  C                          F
I thank You for the cross, I thank You for the cross,
   C/E                     F
I thank You for the cross, my Lord.
   C                       F
I love You for the cross, I love You for the cross,
   C/E                    F    [C/G]    [Last time C]
I love You for the cross, my Lord.  [Repeat]
```

```
F/A    Am    F
Hey,  oh.
C    F   Am   F
Hey, oh, oh.
```

I thank You for the cross. . .

Copyright © 2007 Thankyou Music/Adm by worshiptogether.com songs excl. UK & Europe
adm by kingswaysongs.com tym@kingsway.co.uk. Used by permission.

WHEN IT ALL SEEMS TOO MUCH

Remember

Tré & Tori Sheppard, Mark Prentice,
Paul Baker, Jonny Ravn & Steve Evans

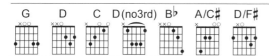

G D C D(no3rd) B♭ A/C♯ D/F♯

Intro: G D G D G C B♭

Verse 1:
      D(no3rd)
When it all seems too much
And the smooth turns rough
And my right way ends up wrong;
When the burden's not light,
I get stuck in the fight
And my worst side comes out strong.

Chorus:
          G   D
And then I remember You
              G   D
And everything that You've done for me.
              G   C
And then I remember when You died on the cross,
      B♭   D(no3rd) B♭ [2.] D(no3rd) B♭
It was You who remembered me.

Verse 2:
Sometimes I can't see
When my pride blinds me,
And my failings fill my mind.
But I hear You calling so deep,
It wakes me from my sleep
To the Love that gives me life.

Ending:
D   A/C♯   D/F♯   G
Hallelujah, You have remembered me.
D   A/C♯   D/F♯   G
Hallelujah, You have remembered me.
D   A/C♯   D/F♯   G
Hallelujah, You have remembered me.
D   A/C♯   D/F♯   G
Hallelujah, You have remembered me.
C   B♭   D(no3rd) B♭ D(no3rd)
I know You have remembered me.

Taken from
AS SURE AS THE STARS
Onehundredhours
SURCD5089

WHEN I WALK THROUGH SUFFERING

(Until the day)

Paul Baloche, Steven Curtis-Chapman, Stuart Garrard,Israel Houghton,
Tim Hughes, Graham Kendrick, Andy Park, Matt Redman,
Martin Smith, Michael W. Smith, Chris Tomlin, Darlene Zschech

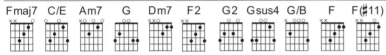

Fmaj7   C/E   Am7   G   Dm7   F2   G2   Gsus4   G/B   F   F(#11)

Verse 1:

     Fmaj7   C/E
When I walk through suffering,
    Am7   G
Let it be that offering,
      Dm7   C/E   F2 G2
Like a fragrance rising.
     Fmaj7   C/E
In the valley of shadow,
      Am7   G
Not to waste my sorrows,
      Dm7   C/E   F2
But to trust and follow.

Chorus:

G   Fmaj7
Until the day
        Am7   G
When You wipe away every tear,
Dm7   C/E   F   G   Fmaj7
   You will   hold me, carry me until the day
        Am7   G
When You take away every fear.
Dm7   C/E   F   [1.Gsus4 G]
  No more   suffering, who can imagine.
                  [Last time G   C]

Verse 2:

So I'll trade my sorrows
For the joy of knowing You,
Sharing Your tomorrow.
With Your comfort, comforting,
Bringing hope from the hope You bring,
My whole life an offering.

Chorus:

G   Fmaj7
Until the day
        Am7   G
When You wipe away every tear,
Dm7   C/E   F   G   Fmaj7
   You will   hold me, carry me until the day
        Am7   G   C/E
When You take away every last fear.
F   G   Am7   G
Who can imagine, who can imagine,
G/B   C   Dm7   C/E   F   F(#11) F
Who can imagine, who can imagine, who?
N.C.
Until the day. . .

Taken from
Compassionart

WHEN MY HEART IS OVERWHELMED

140.

(Lead me to the rock)

Paul Baloche, Steven Curtis-Chapman, Stuart Garrard,Israel Houghton,
Tim Hughes, Graham Kendrick, Andy Park, Matt Redman,
Martin Smith, Michael W. Smith, Chris Tomlin, Darlene Zschech

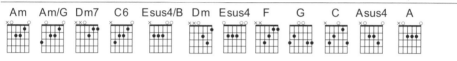

Am Am/G Dm7 C6 Esus4/B Dm Esus4 F G C Asus4 A

Capo 5

Verse 1:
       Am
When my heart is overwhelmed,
      Am/G
And my eyes are blind to You,
     Dm7   C6 Esus4/B
And the pain of life is just too heavy to bear.
       Am
When the mountains seem so high,
        Am/G
And my faith too weak to climb,
Dm7   C6 Esus4/B
Lead me to the rock that is higher than I.

Chorus:
Am   Am/G
Lead me to the rock, lead me to the rock,
Dm   C6 Esus4/B
Lead me to the rock that is higher than I.
A   C6
Lead me to the rock, lead me to the rock,
Dm7   C6 Esus4 [To end Am]
Lead me to the rock that is higher than I.

Verse 2:
When my life is hit with fear,
And I fight to hide the tears,
And I wrestle in my heart to know what to do.
Lord, I'm welling up inside,
But I know you hear my cry;
Jesus, lead me to the rock that is higher than I.

Mid section:
F   G
   You are the rock, and there is no other;
F   G   C
   A tower of strength, You are my shelter.
F
   You are my hope eternal,
G   Asus4 A
   You are the rock that is higher than I.
F Dm   G Em
   You are the rock, and there is no other;
F   Dm   G Em
   A tower of strength, You are my shelter.
F
   You are my hope eternal,
G   Asus4 A
   You are the rock that is higher than I.

Taken from
COMPASSIONART

WHEN NO ONE ELSE WILL WALK BESIDE ME 141.

Walk beside me, Jesus

Johnny Parks & Paula Keenan

Am   G/B   C   G   Em7

Capo 4

Verse 1:

                    C#m(Am)   B/D#(G/B)
When no-one else will walk beside me
E(C)   B(G)
  Through longest hours of deepest night,
                    C#m(Am)   B/D#(G/B)
I hear Your footsteps in the silence,
E(C)   B(G)
  I feel the warmth of Your sweet light.

Verse 2:

When dark times crush my failing spirit,
Confusion racks my quiet hours,
I feel Your love and grace approach me,
I know the touch of higher powers.

Chorus:

          C#m(Am)   B/D#(G/B)
Walk beside me, Jesus,
E(C)   B(G)
  Lend Your Spirit to my own,
        C#m(Am)   B/D#(G/B)
Light this path before me,
E(C)   B(G)   [1.] C#m(Am) B/D#(G/B) E(C)
  Help me find a way back home.

Verse 3:

I feel so far from my redemption,
Doubts assail my peace of mind,
I feel Your hand upon my shoulder,
Peace at last in You I find.

Tag:

        B(G)   C#m(Am)
I know You'll walk with me in this valley,
  B/D#(G/B)   G#m7(Em7)   E(C)
Like You walk with me on the mountain top.

Taken from
BREAK THE SILENCE
Johnny Parks Band
SURCD5095

WHEN WE SING

(Our love is loud)

David Crowder

```
D   Em7  Bm7  G2   D/C#  D/F#
```

Capo 2

Verse 1:
```
          D    Em7          Bm7     G2
When we sing,   hear our songs   to You;
          D    Em7          Bm7     G2
When we dance,    feel us move   to You;
          D    Em7          Bm7     G2
When we laugh,   fill our smiles  with You.
```

Pre chorus:
```
          D              Em7
When we lift our voices louder still,
    Bm7          G2
Can You hear us, can You feel?
```

Chorus:
```
          D              D/C#         Bm7  G2
We love You, Lord, we love You, we love You.
          D              D/C#         Bm7  G2  D  Em7  Bm7  G2
We love You, Lord, we love You, we love You.
```

Verse 2:
When we sing loud, hear our songs to You;
When we dance 'round, feel us move to You;
When we laugh aloud, fill our smiles with You.

```
              D              Em7
And our love is big, our love is loud.
   D/F#                  G2
Fill this place with this love, now.
              D              Em7
And our love is big, our love is loud.
          D/F#                G2
        Fill this place with this love, now. [Repeat]
[2nd time] Fill our lungs  to  sing  it    now.
```

Coda:
```
          D              D/C#
We lift our voices louder still.
      Bm7          G2              [D]
Our God is near, our God is here. [Repeat]
```

Taken from
BEST OF PASSION
(so far)
SURCD5093

WHEN WE SING

(Our love is loud)

Verse 1:

      E   F#m7   C#m7   A2
When we sing,   hear our songs   to You;
      E   F#m7   C#m7   A2
When we dance,   feel us move   to You;
      E   F#m7   C#m7   A2
When we laugh,   fill our smiles   with You.

Pre chorus:

       E   F#m7
When we lift our voices louder still,
  C#m7   A2
Can You hear us, can You feel?

Chorus:

      E   E/D#   C#m7 A2
We love You, Lord, we love You, we love You.
      E   E/D#   C#m7 A2 E F#m7 C#m7 A2
We love You, Lord, we love You, we love You.

Verse 2:

When we sing loud, hear our songs to You;
When we dance 'round, feel us move to You;
When we laugh aloud, fill our smiles with You.

        E   F#m7
And our love is big, our love is loud.
 E/G#   A2
Fill this place with this love, now.
        E   F#m7
And our love is big, our love is loud.
      E/G#   A2
      Fill this place with this love, now. [Repeat]
[2nd time] Fill our lungs to sing it   now.

Coda:

      E   E/D#
We lift our voices louder still.
    C#m7   A2   [E]
Our God is near, our God is here. [Repeat]

Taken from
BEST OF PASSION
(so far)
SURCD5093

WHEN WE WERE IN THE DARKEST NIGHT

God of our yesterdays

Matt Redman

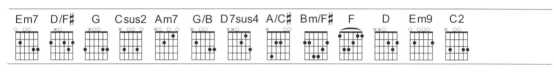

Em7 D/F♯ G Csus2 Am7 G/B D7sus4 A/C♯ Bm/F♯ F D Em9 C2

Verse 1:

Em7
When we were in the darkest night,
    D/F♯   G   Csus2
And wondered if our eyes would ever see the light,
You were there, Lord.

Em7
When we were in the stormy gale,
    D/F♯   G   CSus2
And wondered if we'd ever live in peace again,
You were there, Lord.

                  Am7
You were there in the struggle,
              G/B
You were there in the fight,
              Csus2   D7sus4
You were there all the time.

Verse 2:

So, whatever lies ahead,
Whatever road our grateful hearts will come to tread,
You'll be there, Lord.
And we will fix our eyes on You,
And know that there is grace enough to see us through;
You'll be there, Lord.
You'll be there in the struggle,
You'll be there in the fight,
You'll be there all the time.

Chorus:

    G
We praise You, the God of our yesterdays.
    Em7
We praise You, the God who is here today.
    A/C♯   Am7 G/B Csus2
We praise You, our God, as tomor - row comes.
[2nd & 3rd time:]
           G
We thank you for grace in our yesterdays,
       Bm/F♯
We thank You for peace in our hearts today,
      A/C♯   Am7 G/B Csus2
We thank You, our joy. As tomor - row comes,
       Am7 G/B Csus2
We will trust You God.

Mid section:

                            G/B
You're always closer than we know,
Csus2   G/B
Always more involved and in control.
Csus2   G/B
  We will trust our lives to You,
      F   D/F♯   D
The One who was and is and is to come.

Ending:
| Am7 G/B | Csus2 / / / ||: Em9 / / / | D/F♯ / G / | C2 / / / | / / / / :||

Last time: | Em9 / / / | D/F♯ / G / | C2 / / / | / / / G/B | C2 ||

Taken from
GOD OF THIS CITY
Passion
SURCD5126

WHO CAN DESCRIBE YOU TO ME

144.
Andy Smith

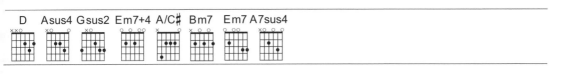

D   Asus4 Gsus2 Em7+4 A/C# Bm7   Em7 A7sus4

Capo 2

Verse 1:
D
Who can describe You to me?
Asus4
You are such a mystery.
D   Asus4
Greater things no one has seen
                          Gsus2
And I've found that oh,
          Em7+4
I love You so.

Chorus:
          D   A/C#
Jesus, redeemer,
          Bm7   G
You are the prince of peace,
              D   A/C#
My strong deliv'rer,
              Bm7   A
You gave Your life for me.
              Em7
I've found that oh,
          A7sus4   A   [D]
I love You so.

Verse 2:
You are the same yesterday,
Today and forevermore,
Yet You chose to lay Yourself down.
And I've found that oh,
I love You so.

Taken from
BREATHE
Andy Smith
SURCD5073

WHO CAN DESCRIBE YOU TO ME

Andy Smith

Verse 1:
E
Who can describe You to me?
Bsus4
You are such a mystery.
E   Bsus4
Greater things no one has seen
                          Asus2
And I've found that oh,
          F#m7+4
I love You so.

Chorus:
          E   B/D#
Jesus, redeemer,
          C#m7   G
You are the prince of peace,
          E   B/D#
My strong deliv'rer,
          C#m7   B
You gave Your life for me.
          F#m7
I've found that oh,
          B7sus4   B   [E]
I love You so.

Verse 2:
You are the same yesterday,
Today and forevermore,
Yet You chose to lay Yourself down.
And I've found that oh,
I love You so.

Taken from
BREATHE
Andy Smith
SURCD5073

WHO DO WE SAY
(His renown)

145.

Nathan Nockles
& Christy Nockles

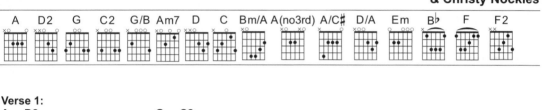

A D2 G C2 G/B Am7 D C Bm/A A(no3rd) A/C# D/A Em B♭ F F2

Verse 1:
A   D2   G   C2
   Who do we say that He is   with our lives?
A   D2   G   C2
   Who do we say that He is   with the words that we say?
A   D2   G   C2   G/B   Am7 G/B C2
   Who do we say that He is   for the little eyes watching you and me?

Verse 2:
Where are we going with His heart with our lives?
Where are we going with His heart in the words that we say?
Where are we going with His heart for the little eyes watching you and me?

Bridge:
   D   C
We can't just wash our hands of this,
D   C   D   C
   And walk away, and blame the ones before us;
           D   Am
'Cause it's easier to say
       Bm/A   Am7
Than to listen to His heart
       Bm/A   A(no3rd)
Beating for the coming age.

Chorus:
         D   A   G   A
So let the hands go up around the world in surrender.
            D   A   G   A
And let the voices echo out a new sound,
         D   A/C# G/B   D/A
So the ones who come behind us will follow in His name,
      G   A   [1. C D   C   D Em] [2. D A] [3. B♭]
And see the greatness of His renown. [4. C2   D C2   D   C2 G/B Asus2]

Verse 3:
Who will we say that He is with our lives?
Who will we say that He is in the words that we say?
Who will we say that He is for the little eyes watching you and me?

Mid section:
Am7   B♭ C   B♭
   We are a doorway and a window to the truth.
Am7   F   C/E
   We have one passage of time.
B♭   Am7 B♭   C
   What will we say then, how will we live?
B♭   Am7   F2 C2/E   D A G A D A G A
   This burning passion is a gift,   is a gift.   Let the . . .

Copyright © 1997 Sweater Weather Music / Word Music / Rocketown Music

Taken from
BEST OF PASSION
(so far)
SURCD5093

WHO I HAVE BECOME IN YOU

146.

(Highly favoured)

Paul Baloche, Steven Curtis-Chapman, Stuart Garrard,Israel Houghton,
Tim Hughes, Graham Kendrick, Andy Park, Matt Redman,
Martin Smith, Michael W. Smith, Chris Tomlin, Darlene Zschech

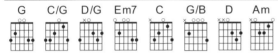

G C/G D/G Em7 C G/B D Am

Verse 1:
```
G                C/G    G
   Who I have become in You
                      D/G
Is grace beyond all measure.
G           C/G    G
In the light of all You are,
               D/G   G
Who am I to be found here.
```

Verse 2:
Who I have become in You
Is grace beyond all measure;
Raised to life and crowned with love:
Jesus Yours forever.

Chorus:
```
Em7        C
Majesty and mercy,
G/B           D
Lead me in this moment;
     C        G/B
How can it be that I have been
Am             D
Chosen by the King?
Em7           C
There's no greater honour,
G           D
There's no greater treasure,
     C           G/B
Than to be known and loved by You:
Am7      D
I am highly favoured,
C         Am  G
I am highly favoured.
```

Verse 3:
A child of grace I have become,
Adopted into favour;
Now I sing Your Spirit's song:
Crying 'Abba Father'.

Taken from
COMPASSIONART

WILL YOU GO TO THE ENDS OF THE EARTH? 147.

Yes, Lord

Jorge Mhondera & Quentin Delport

Cmaj7 Am7 Em7 Em

Cmaj7   Am7
   Will you go to the ends of the earth?
     Em7
Say, 'yes, Lord'. (Yes, Lord.)
Cmaj7   Am7
   Sing it out to the hurt and the lost;
     Em7
Say, 'yes, Lord'. (Yes, Lord.)
Cmaj7   Am7
   Will you shine your light in the dark?
     Em7
Say, 'yes, Lord'. (Yes, Lord.)
Cmaj7   Am7
   Shine it out for the world to see;
     Em7
Say, 'yes, Lord'. (Yes, Lord.)

       Cmaj7   Am7
We're singing: 'yes, Lord'. (Yes, Lord.)
       Em7
We're singing: 'yes, Lord'. (Yes, Lord.)
       Cmaj7   Am7
We're singing: 'yes, Lord'. (Yes, Lord.)
       Em7
We're singing: 'yes, Lord'. (Yes, Lord.)

       Cmaj7   Am7
We're singing: 'yes, yes, Lord'. (Yes, yes, Lord.)
       Em7
We're singing: 'yes, yes, Lord'. (Yes, yes, Lord.)
       Cmaj7   Am7
We're singing: 'yes, yes, Lord'. (Yes, yes, Lord.)
       Em7
We're singing: 'yes, yes, Lord'. (Yes, yes, Lord.)

| Cmaj7 | Am7 | Em ||

Taken from
LIVING FOR YOUR GLORY
Soul Survivor 2007
SURCD5108

WITH EVERY RISING SUN

The troubles are over

Johnny & Cathy Parks
& Claire Hamilton

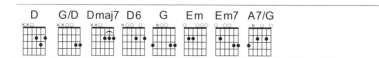

D G/D Dmaj7 D6 G Em Em7 A7/G

Verse 1:
```
       D              G/D
With every rising sun,
D                    Dmaj7
   Every evening's fall
D6          G
We have prevailed.
                Em
You've been our hope.
       D              G/D
And through the darkest days,
D                    Dmaj7
   Through the spilling of blood,
D6          G
You heard our prayers
                Em
And the troubles are o'er,
                D
The troubles are o'er!
[2nd & 3rd time:]
                    Em7
The troubles are o'er!
```

Verse 2:
We've broken hardened ground,
Sown seeds with faith;
You've seen our work,
A harvest awaits.
You've softened hardened hearts,
Broken heavy chains,
Given Your grace,
Amazing grace,
And the troubles are o'er!

Verse 3:
Let the Prince of Peace
Reign in our land:
North and south,
East and west.
When the Kingdom comes,
Free we will stand,
And we'll declare:
Our troubles are o'er,
Our troubles are o'er!

Ending:
```
D     G/D    D       G/D
All Your ways are higher and higher.
G   A7/G  G      Em7           (D)
You bring peace to those who cry out.   [Repeat]
```

Taken from
BREAK THE SILENCE
Johnny Parks Band
SURCD5095

WORSHIP THE LORD

Al Gordon

G   C2   Em7   G/B   Dsus4   D

Verse 1:
G   C2
Worship the Lord in the beauty of holiness,
              Em7   C2
With awe and with reverence, bow to adore.
              G   C2
You are my Lord, You are my holiness,
        Em7   C2
Jesus, my righteousness, I worship You, Lord.

Chorus:
                    G/B   C2
I'm living for Your glory,
                    Em7   Dsus4
I'm living for the name above all names.
                    G/B   C2
No one else is worthy,
                    Em7   Dsus4   D
No one else can ever take Your place.

Verse 2:
I worship You, Lord, in beautiful holiness,
Lifting up reverence, I bow to adore.
I give You my all, surrendering everything,
My everyday offering - to worship You Lord.

Mid section:
    C
You are high and lifted up,
D
High and lifted up,
Em7   D/F♯
High and lifted up.   (x 4)

WORTHY IS THE LAMB

Andy Ferrett
& Marc James

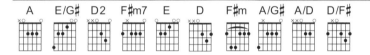

A   E/G# D2 F#m7 E   D   F#m A/G# A/D D/F#

Verse 1:
A   E/G#   D2
Worthy is   the Lamb
A   E/G#   D2
Who was slain   for sin.
A   E/G#   D2
Worthy is   the One who died for us;
      F#m7   E/G#   D2
Receive   all power and praise.

Chorus:
                     A
We give You our lives,
                        E
'Cos You're worthy of praise;
                F#m
We lift up Your name
                  D
And walk in Your ways.
                 A
We raise up our hands,
                  E
We raise up one voice;
         D
Every breath that we breathe,
                          [A A/G# A/D]
Every day that we live is for You. [A to end]

Verse 2:
Holy is the Lord,
Who was and is to come.
Holy is our God, who sits on high;
Receive all glory here.

Mid section:
E/G#   D
    All honour,
E/G#   D
    All blessing and power to You.
E/G# D
    All wisdom,
E   D/F#   E/G#
    All glory and praise to Your name.
            D
Glory and praise,
E   D/F#
  Glory and praise,
E/G#   D
  Glory and praise.

Copyright © 2008 Thankyou Music/Adm by worshiptogether.com songs excl. UK & Europe
adm by kingswaysongs.com tym@kingsway.co.uk. Used by permission.

WORTHY, YOU ARE WORTHY

151.

Worthy

Matt Redman

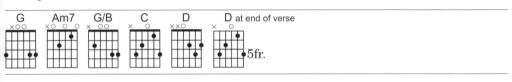

(Capo 4)

Verse 1:
B (G)   C#m7 (Am7)
Worthy, You are worthy
    B/D# (G/B) E (C)
Much more worthy than I know
B (G) C#m7 (Am7)
I cannot imagine
    B/D# (G/B) E (C)
Just how glorious You are
F# (D)   E (C)
 And I cannot begin to tell
  B/D# (G/B)   E (C)
How deep the love You bring
F# (D)   E (C)
 O Lord, my ears have heard of You
  B/D# (G/B)   E (C) F# (D) E (C) F# (D) E(C)
But now my eyes have seen

Chorus:
   B (G)   C#m7 (Am7)
You're worthy, You're worthy
   B/D# (G/B) E (C)
You're worthy
   B (G)   C#m7 (Am7)
You're worthy to be praised
  B/D# (G/B) E (C)
Forever and a day   (repeat)

Verse 2:
Glory, I give glory to the One who saved my soul
You found me and You freed me from the shame that was my own
And I cannot begin to tell how merciful You've been
O Lord, my ears have heard of You but now my eyes have seen

Chorus 2: (high)
You're worthy, You're worthy, You're worthy
You're worthy to be praised, forever and a day
Your glory, Your glory, Your glory
Your glory reaches high, so high above the heavens

Taken from
FACEDOWN
Matt Redman
SURCD5007
and
LIVING FOR YOUR GLORY
Soul Survivor Live 2007
SURCD5108

YEAH, WE SHINE, WE SHINE

We shine

Steve Fee & Louie Giglio

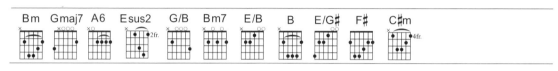

Verse 1:
```
        Bm
Yeah, we shine, we shine the light of God.
            Gmaj7
And when we speak, we speak with words of love.
            A6
And when we dance, we may get a little wild,
              Esus2
'Cause we're the people of God,
Yeah, the people of God.
        Bm
And when we sing, we sing the angel's songs,
    Gmaj7
The ones they're singing around the throne.
              A6
Yeah, yeah, we worship the King with everything that we are,
                Esus2
'Cause we're the people of God,
Yeah, the people of God. Yeah!
```

Bridge:
```
     Bm
And now is the time for the people to rise.
G/B
Lift up a shout, everybody cry out.
Bm7
Raise your voice, shout out a noise,
E/B
Dance a dance of joy. (One! Two! Three! Four!)
```

Chorus:
```
B             E/G#
We are the redeemed.
We are the ones who are free,
F#                   Esus2  C#m
  And we belong to Jesus.
B             E/G#
We are now alive,
And in this world we will shine,
F#                   Esus2  [1.] Bm7
  And we belong to Jesus.
```

Mid section:
```
| Bm | Bm | Gmaj7 | Gmaj7 | A6 | A6 | E | E |
             Bm
Yeah, we're going into all the world,
         Gmaj7
We're carrying the light of Jesus.
           A6
And we shine, we shine
           E
In the darkest place, we shine.   [Repeat]
```

Verse 2:
```
Where the Spirit of God is, freedom reigns.
So, come on, come on,
Throw off your prison chains.
We're liberated by a King,
Only freedom remains
For the people of God, yeah,
The people of God, yeah.
We're living in a kingdom that will never end;
We're living in the power that defeated sin.
So come on, everybody,
Let your praise begin.
Jesus is alive, and He's coming again.
```

Taken from
GOD OF THIS CITY
Passion
SURCD5126

YOU ARE SO GOOD TO ME

(Shout from the roof)

Paul Oakley
& Chris Spring

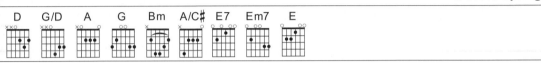

Verse 1:

D   G/D
You are so good to me,
D   G/D A   G
I did not know You,   but I heard You call out my name.
A   G   D   G/D
I couldn't see You, but I   felt You reach into my heart,
D   G/D
Take all my fear and shame,
A   G   A   G
Pour all Your kindness in, You turned my life around.
   Bm   A/C#   Bm
And now You have opened up my eyes
   A/C#   D   E7
To the mystery of Your grace.

Chorus:

G   D
I could sing, I could dance in the street,
G   A   G   D
I could shout from the roof how Your love set me free,
G   A
How this gospel is true.
G   D   G   A
You're the Way, You're Truth, You're the Life
          G   Em7
And I will always follow You,
                 G   D   [G/D D G/D A G A G]
You make all things new, Jesus, You are good.

Mid section:

E   G   E   G
There is only one way, there is only one Name.
E   G   E   G   D G/D A G D G/D
There is only one God, Jesus, You, and You alone can save.
A   G
I could sing, I could dance . . .

Verse 2:
You are like no one else;
You reign forever, Jesus. Name above every name,
Today, forever, You're the same.
You conquered sin for me, Your blood has made me clean.
Your mercy covers me,
Your goodness leads me on,
And now I can never be the same:
You alone deserve my praise.

Taken from
SHOUT FROM THE ROOF
Newday 2006
SURCD5075

YOU ARE SO GOOD TO ME

(Shout from the roof)

Paul Oakley
& Chris Spring

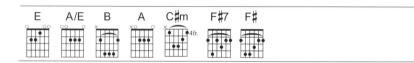

E   A/E   B   A   C#m   F#7   F#

Verse 1:
```
E                  A/E
   You are so good to me,
E                  A/E  B              A
   I did not know You,   but I heard You call out my name.
B                A    E            A/E
   I couldn't see You, but I   felt You reach into my heart,
E                  A/E
   Take all my fear and shame,
B                A      B                    A
   Pour all Your kindness in,  You turned my life around.
   C#m      B/D#              C#m
And now You have opened up my eyes
   B/D#    E              F#7
To the mystery of Your grace.
```

Chorus:
```
A                     E
   I could sing, I could dance in the street,
A         B        A         E
I could shout from the roof how Your love set me free,
A         B
How this gospel is true.
A         E        A         B
You're the Way, You're Truth, You're the Life
            A            F#m7
And I will always follow You,
                A              E    [A/E  E  A/E  B  A  B  A]
You make all things new, Jesus, You are good.
```

Mid section:
```
F#        A       F#        A
   There is only one way, there is only one Name.
F#        A       F#        A                    E  A/E  B  A  E  A/E
   There is only one God, Jesus, You, and You alone can save.
B         A
   I could sing, I could dance . . .
```

Verse 2:
You are like no one else;
You reign forever, Jesus. Name above every name,
Today, forever, You're the same.
You conquered sin for me, Your blood has made me clean.
Your mercy covers me,
Your goodness leads me on,
And now I can never be the same:
You alone deserve my praise.

Taken from
SHOUT FROM THE ROOF
Newday 2006
SURCD5075

YOU ARE THE FIRST

(Glory in the highest)

154.

Chris Tomlin, Ed Cash, Matt Redman,
Jesse Reeves & Daniel Carson

C   G/B   Am7   F   Fmaj7   Dm7   C/E   F/C

Verse 1:

C   G/B
    You are the first, You go before,
Am7   F
    You are the last, Lord, You're the encore.
C   G
    You're name's in lights for all to see,
Am7   F
    The starry host declare Your glory.

Chorus:

         Fmaj7   G
Glory in the highest,
         Am7   G
Glory in the highest,
         Dm7   C/E   F
Glory in the highest.

Verse 2:
Apart from You there is no God,
Light of the World, the bright and morning star.
Your name will shine for all to see,
You are the One, You are my glory.

G   Am7   F
    And no one else could ever compare
          G
To You, Lord.
       Am7   F
All the earth together declare:

         C   F
Glory in the highest,
         C   F
Glory in the highest,
         C   F
Glory in the highest,
         C   F
To You, Lord,   to You, Lord. [Repeat]

C
All the earth will sing Your praise,
      F
The moon and stars, the sun and rain.
   C
Every nation will proclaim,
    F
That You are God, and You will reign.
C   F
Glory, glory, hallelujah, glory, glory to You, Lord.
C   F   C   F/C   F   F/C   C
Glory, glory, hallelujah, hallelujah.

Taken from
SEE THE MORNING
Chris Tomlin
SURCD5084

YOU ARE THE ONLY ONE I NEED

(You alone)

Jack Parker
& David Crowder

Capo 2

Verse:
D   D/F♯   G2   D
You are the only One I need,
D/F♯ D2   D
I bow all of me at Your feet.
D/F♯ G2   D   D/F♯   G2
I   worship You alone.
D   D/F♯ G2   D
You have given me more than I
D/F♯ G2   D
Could ever have wanted and I
D/F♯   G2   D   D/F♯   G2
Want to give You my heart and my soul.

Chorus:
D   D/F♯   G
You   alone are Father,
    D   D/F♯ G
And You   alone are good;
D   D/F♯   G
You   alone are Saviour,
    D   D/F♯   [1. D   D/F♯ G2   D   D/F♯   G2]
And You   alone are God. [2. A   D]

Taken from
SEE THE MORNING
Chris Tomlin
SURCD5084

YOU ARE THE ONLY ONE I NEED

(You alone)

155.
Jack Parker
& David Crowder

Verse:
E   E/G♯   A2   E
You are the only One I need,
E/G♯ E2   E
I bow all of me at Your feet.
E/G♯ A2   E   E/G♯   A2
I   worship You alone.
E   E/G♯ A2   E
You have given me more than I
E/G♯ A2   E
Could ever have wanted and I
E/G♯   A2   E   E/G♯   A2
Want to give You my heart and my soul.

Chorus:
E   E/G♯   A
You   alone are Father,
      E   E/G♯ A
And You   alone are good;
E   E/G♯   A
You   alone are Saviour,
      E   E/G♯   [1. E   E/G♯ A2   E   E/G♯   A2]
And You   alone are God. [2. B   E]

Taken from
SEE THE MORNING
Chris Tomlin
SURCD5084

YOU ARE THE ROCK

(Hallelujah)

Verse 1:
```
F                        Fmaj7
   You are the Rock that I cling to,
Bb
   You are my strength and my song.
F                        Fmaj7/A
   You give me shelter and refuge,
Bb                          Csus4
   You are the one who is strong.
Bb                          Csus4
   Was lost, now I'm found,
                              Bb
You turned me around,
                        Csus4
And standing on Your promise I sing:
```

Chorus:
```
F                    Csus4
   Hallelujah,  to the Lord Almighty,
Gm7          Bb        Csus4     F
   Hallelujah, to the One who saved my soul.
                    Csus4
Hallelujah, 'cause I've found mercy:
Gm7              Bb          Csus4      [Bb   Csus4]
Living free, I will be walking in the fullness of life. [Last x F   Csus4   Gm7   Bb   Csus4   F]
```

Verse 2:
```
You are the only salvation,
You are the end and the start.
You are the God of creation,
You are the King of my heart.
Once blind, now I see.
You've set this life free;
And standing in Your goodness I sing.
```

Mid section:
```
F                    Cadd4/E
   Let angels above,
                         Gm7
Amazed at such love
                    Bb        Csus4
Sing: 'worthy is the King of grace'.
F                    Cadd4/E
   Let voices ring out,
                         Gm7
Let all the earth shout;
                    Bb        Csus4  Bb  Csus4  Bb/D   Csus4
You alone shall have our praise.
```

YOU ARE THE ROCK

(Hallelujah)

156.

Martin Cooper

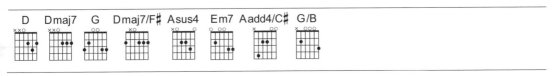

Chord names: D Dmaj7 G Dmaj7/F♯ Asus4 Em7 Aadd4/C♯ G/B

Capo 3:

Verse 1:
D   Dmaj7
  You are the Rock that I cling to,
G
  You are my strength and my song.
D   Dmaj7/F♯
  You give me shelter and refuge,
G   Asus4
  You are the one who is strong.
G   Asus4
  Was lost, now I'm found,
               G
You turned me around,
             Asus4
And standing on Your promise I sing:

Chorus:
D   Asus4
  Hallelujah, to the Lord Almighty,
Em7   G   Asus4   D
  Hallelujah, to the One who saved my soul.
          Asus4
Hallelujah, 'cause I've found mercy:
Em7   G   Asus4   [G   Asus4]
Living free, I will be walking in the fullness of life. [Last x D   Asus4   Em7   G   Asus4   D]

Verse 2:
You are the only salvation,
You are the end and the start.
You are the God of creation,
You are the King of my heart.
Once blind, now I see.
You've set this life free;
And standing in Your goodness I sing.

Mid section
D   Aadd4/C♯
  Let angels above,
          Em7
Amazed at such love
          G   Asus4
Sing: 'worthy is the King of grace'.
D   Aadd4/C♯
  Let voices ring out,
          Em7
Let all the earth shout;
          G   Asus4 G Asus4   G/B   Asus4
You alone shall have our praise.

YOU GIVE ME STRENGTH

157.

(Catch me)

Paul Baloche, Steven Curtis-Chapman, Stuart Garrard, Israel Houghton,
Tim Hughes, Graham Kendrick, Andy Park, Matt Redman,
Martin Smith, Michael W. Smith, Chris Tomlin, Darlene Zschech

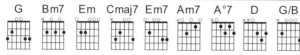

G   Bm7   Em   Cmaj7   Em7   Am7   A°7   D   G/B

Capo 3:
Verse:
G
You give me strength to find a way,
Bm7   Em
  Give me hope to fight each day;
Cmaj7
All I need is found in You.
G   Bm7
Grace, a gift You love to give,
            Em7
The only way to live,
 Cmaj7
All I need is found in You,
Am7   A°7
  What ever life brings,

Chorus:
     G   D
Whenever I fall I know You'll catch me,
    Am7   Cmaj7   D
Whenever I'm down You're there to lift me,
     G   Bm7
Where ever I go I know You're with me,
    Am7   Cmaj7
You are with me, always You are with me.

Mid section:
D   Cmaj7
Oh, You're my shelter, You're my home
               G
You're my peace when I'm alone,
            D
My peace whan I'm alone.
               Cmaj7
Oh, You're my greatest dream come true,
           Em7
Now I'm so in love with You,
        D
I'm so in love with You,
   Cmaj7
So in love with You.

Coda:
     Cmaj7   Am7   G/B   Cmaj7
You are with me, You are with me, always You are with me,
      Am7
You are with me, always You are with me.

Taken from
COMPASSIONART

YOU HAVE LOVED ME

(Father me)

158.
Paul Oakley

Verse 1:
```
D                  A/D               G/B   A7sus4
You have loved me with such perfect love,
D               A/D             G/B   A7sus4
Fathered me with such a tender touch.
Em7                 D          A7sus4
  Your faithfulness surrounds my soul,
Em7           A7sus4
  Your mercy lifts my head.
D             Em7   A7sus4   D     Em7  A7sus4
How could I repay all You have done?
```

Chorus:
```
         D2
Father me,
      G       A7sus4    D2
Faithful Father. Father me;
       Em7     A7sus4  D2
No one else could e - ver be
           G       A7sus4 D  [G  A7sus4]
The perfect Father God to me.
```

Verse 2:
You now clothe me with Your righteousness,
Hide me in the shadow of Your wings.
And even in my darkest days,
Your light will guide my way.
Hallelujah to the King of grace.

Taken from
SHOUT FROM THE ROOF
Newday 2006
SURCD5075

YOU HAVE SHOWN US

Paul Baloche, Steven Curtis-Chapman, Stuart Garrard,Israel Houghton,
Tim Hughes, Graham Kendrick, Andy Park, Matt Redman,
Martin Smith, Michael W. Smith, Chris Tomlin, Darlene Zschech

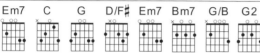

Em7   C   G   D/F♯   Em7   Bm7   G/B   G2

Verse 1:
        Em7   C   G
You have shown us, O God, what is good.
        Em7   C   G
You have shown us, O Lord, what You require.
        Em7   C   G   D/F♯
You have heard all our songs, how we long to worship You,
        Em7   C   D
Yet You've taught us the offering You desire.

Chorus:
    C   D   Em7 Bm7
To do justly and to love mercy,
        C   D   Em7
And to walk humbly with You God.
          C   D   Em7 Bm7
You said to do justly, and to love mercy,
       C   D   [1.2. G]
And to walk humbly with You, God. [3. Em7 G Chorus repeat]

Verse 2:
You have shown us the riches of Your love,
You have shown us Your heart for those in need.
Lord, You're opening our ears to the cries of the poor;
You have called us to be Your hands and feet.

Mid section:
         D
To the oppressed and the broken,
    Em7   G/B
To the widow and the orphan,
      C   D   G2
Let the river of Your justice flow through us.   [Repeat]

Taken from
COMPASSIONART

YOU HOLD THE BROKEN-HEARTED
160.

God of hope

James Gregory & Guy Bastable

C	F	G	G/B	Am	Em7

Verse 1:

C   F   G
You hold the broken-hearted,
C   F   G
You stand before the weak.
C   F   G
You go to those in darkness
Am   F G
And so must we.

Verse 2:

Your heart is for the outcast,
For those we call the least.
You lift the broken spirit
And so must we.

Chorus:

          C   G/B
God of hope, God of futures,
       F   G   Am
You can take a broken heart and make it sing.
G/B   C   G/B   Em7
God of life, new tomorrows,
       F   G   Am G/B   [1.] | C | F G | C | F G |
You can shine the light that changes everything.
[2.]
       F   G   C
You can shine the light that changes everything.

Verse 3:

You go to those forgotten,
The faces we don't see.
You give Your life to save them
And so must we.

Mid section:

               Em7   F
God who speaks, opens graves.
         G   Am
With one word, our God saves!
               Em7   F
God who speaks, opens graves.
         G   Am G/B
With one word, our God saves!

Ending:

       F   G   Am
You can shine the light that changes everything.   [Repeat]
[Last time:]
       F
You can shine the light that changes everything.

YOU KNOW ME COMPLETELY

(Forevermore)

Vicky Beeching
& Marc Byrd

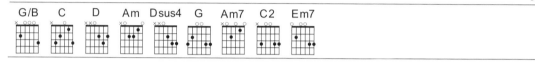

G/B   C   D   Am   Dsus4   G   Am7   C2   Em7

Capo 1

Verse 1:
G/B   C
  You know me completely
D   C
  Like no other could.
G/B   C
  You love me so freely,
D   C   Am
  When no other would.
              C
Your love's a mystery.

Chorus
Am   C   Dsus4
  For all eternity I'll be with You.
G   Am7   C2
You have won my heart forevermore.
G   Am7   C2
You are mine and I'm forever Yours.
Em7   C
You are my desire,
    Am   C
My treasure in this life.
    Em7   D   C
And You have won my heart forevermore.

Verse 2:
One day I will see You
Standing face to face.
One day I'll run into
My Saviour's strong embrace.
It's such a mystery.

D   C
Jesus, how I love You.
D   C   Am
Jesus, how I love You.
   C   Am
My heart is Yours forevermore.
G
You have won my heart forevermore.

Taken from
PAINTING THE INVISIBLE
Vicky Beeching
SURCD5091

YOU KNOW ME COMPLETELY

(Forevermore)

Verse 1:
A♭/C   D♭
  You know me completely
E♭   D♭
  Like no other could.
A♭/C   D♭
  You love me so freely,
E♭   D♭   B♭m
  When no other would.
                 D♭
Your love's a mystery.

Chorus
B♭m   D♭   E♭sus4
  For all eternity I'll be with You.
A♭   B♭m7   D♭2
You have won my heart forevermore.
A♭   B♭m7   D♭2
You are mine and I'm forever Yours.
Fm7   D♭
You are my desire,
  B♭m   D♭
My treasure in this life.
   Fm7   E♭   D♭
And You have won my heart forevermore.

Verse 2:
One day I will see You
Standing face to face.
One day I'll run into
My Saviour's strong embrace.
It's such a mystery.

E♭   D♭
Jesus, how I love You.
E♭   D♭   B♭m
Jesus, how I love You.
   D♭   B♭m
My heart is Yours forevermore.
A♭
You have won my heart forevermore.

Taken from
PAINTING THE INVISIBLE
Vicky Beeching
SURCD5091

YOUNG AND OLD
162.

(So great)

Paul Baloche, Steven Curtis-Chapman, Stuart Garrard, Israel Houghton,
Tim Hughes, Graham Kendrick, Andy Park, Matt Redman,
Martin Smith, Michael W. Smith, Chris Tomlin, Darlene Zschech

D   C   A/D   G/D   Dsus4   A/C♯   G/B   A   Asus4/G   G   Bm7   Bm   D/F♯   D/A

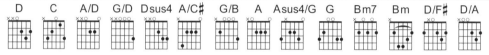

Capo 3

Verse 1:
D   C
Young and old, rich and poor,
D   A/D   G/D   D
Weak and strong, everyone,
               Dsus4
Come and rest, you are safe
D   A/C♯ G/B   D
In the arms of Jesus.

Bridge:
A   Asus4/G D/F♯
  For He is   good,
A   G   A
  For He is faithful.

Chorus:
      D Bm7   A
So great, so great,
    D/F♯   G   D/A A
And Your love endures for ever.
        D Bm7   A
To the end of the age,
    D/F♯ Bm   G   D/A A [1. D Dsus4] [To end D/A A D]
Oh, Your love endures for e - ver   [more.]

Verse 2:
Beautiful, majesty,
Glorious, holy One.
Rugged cross, sovereign grace,
Oh, the blood of Jesus.

Taken from
COMPASSIONART

YOU REACH BEYOND IMAGINATION

163.

(The way You father me)

Eoghan Heaslip
& David Gate

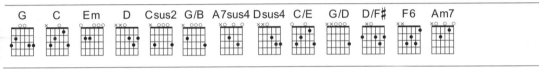

Capo 3

Verse:
```
    G                   C
You reach beyond imagination,
    G                   C
With a love outside of understanding.
    Em              C
You touch the lives of all Your children
    G       D         Csus2
With beauty and goodness.
    G                   C
You know my words before they're spoken.
    G                   C
You hear each cry, my every passion.
    Em                  C
You draw me close and lead me into
    G/B       D         Csus2
Your beauty and goodness.
```

Chorus:
```
G           A7sus4
Wonderful, intimate,
G/B     D           Dsus4   D
Beautiful God of love.
      Em          C
You have always been faithful in
    G/B         D       [1. G/B  C/E  G/D  C]
The way that You father me. [2. G]
                         [3. G/B  C/E  G/D  C  G]
```

Mid section:
```
          G             D/F♯
Our God is good, our God is faithful,
        F6              C
Our God is strong, our God is able.
          G             D/F♯
Our God is good, our God is faithful,
        F6              C/E  C  G  Am7  Em  C/D
Our God is strong, our God is able.
```

YOU'RE CLOSER THAN OUR TROUBLES

You are God

Charlie Hall

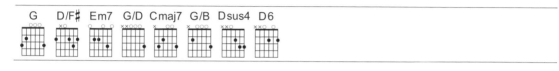

G   D/F# Em7   G/D Cmaj7 G/B Dsus4 D6

Verse 1:
G   D/F#   Em7   G/D
  You're closer than our troubles,
Cmaj7 G/B   Cmaj7 Dsus4
  More present than any danger,
G   D/F#   Em7   G/D
  More grand than gold and silver.
Cmaj7 G/B   Cmaj7   D   G D/F# Em7 G/D Cmaj7 G/B Cmaj7 Dsus4
  You are God,   You are God.

Verse 2:
You're the joy of man's desire,
You are Father, satisfier.
We are stunned with wide-eyed wonder.
You are God, You are God.

Chorus:
G   D/F#
  You fill our hearts with love and faith.
Em7   Dsus4
  You fight for us, You make us brave.
Cmaj7   G/B   Cmaj7   D6
  You are God,   You are God.
G   D/F#
  You walk with us, You lead us on.
Em7   Dsus4
  Faith, hope and love wakes up with dawn.
Cmaj7   G/B   Cmaj7   D6
  You are God,   You are God.

Mid section:
| G/B | Cmaj7 | D6 | D6 |
| G/B | Cmaj7 | D6 | D6 |
D6   G/B Cmaj7   D6   G/B   Cmaj7 D6
  And life   flows from God, it flows from God.
D6   G/B Cmaj7   D6   G/B   Cmaj7 D6
  And life   flows from God, it flows from God.
D6   G/B Cmaj7   D6   G/B   Cmaj7 D6
  And life   flows from God, it flows from God.
D6   G/B Cmaj7   D6   G/B   Cmaj7 D6
  And life   flows from God, it flows from God.

Taken from
GOD OF THIS CITY
Passion
SURCD5126

YOU'RE EVERYTHING

We won't be quiet

Jack Parker, David Crowder
& Mike Hogan

D5   Asus4 Gsus2

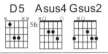

Capo 1(D)

Verse:
Eb5(D5)   Bbsus4(Asus4) Absus2(Gsus2)
  You're everything we could ever want,
Eb5(D5)   Bbsus4(Asus4) Absus2(Gsus2)
  You're everything we could ever need.
Eb5(D5)   Bbsus4(Asus4) Absus2(Gsus2)
  You're the reason we're coming here,
Eb5(D5)   Bbsus4(Asus4) Absus2(Gsus2)
  You're the reason we're gonna sing.   [Repeat]

Chorus:
Eb5(D5)   Bbsus4(Asus4) Absus2(Gsus2)
  We'll shout it out loud from the rooftop:
Eb5(D5)   Bbsus4(Asus4) Absus2(Gsus2)
  We won't be qui - - - - - - - et.
Eb5(D5)   Bbsus4(Asus4) Absus2(Gsus2)
  We've fallen for You hard, and we can't stop.
Eb5(D5)   Bbsus4(Asus4) Absus2(Gsus2)
  We won't deny   it.

Fill:

| Eb5(D5) / Bbsus4(Asus4) / | Absus2(Gsus2) |
| Eb5(D5) / Bbsus4(Asus4) / | Absus2(Gsus2) |

Ending:

| Eb5(D5) | Bbsus4(Asus4) / Absus2(Gsus2) / |
| Eb5(D5) | Bbsus4(Asus4) / Absus2(Gsus2) / |
| Eb5(D5) |

Taken from
REMEDY
David Crowder Band
SURCD5101

YOU'RE MIGHTY AND POWERFUL TO SAVE   166.

(Salvation song)

Andy Smith

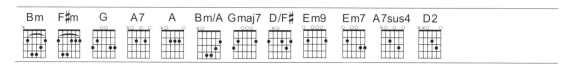

Bm   F#m   G   A7   A   Bm/A   Gmaj7   D/F#   Em9   Em7   A7sus4   D2

Verse 1:
Bm   F#m
  You're mighty   and powerful to save.
Bm   F#m
  My feet bare,   my fear for You displayed.
Bm   F#m
  You touch me,   and disintegrate my blame.
G   A7
  I'll never be the same.

Chorus:
       G   A
And our faces now uncovered
  Bm   Bm/A   Gmaj7
Reveal the awesome glory of Your Son.
       G   A
Will You put Your voice within me,
  Bm   Bm/A   Gmaj7   D/F#
So they can hear the sweet song that You sing.
Em9   [1. G D/F# D   Em7 D/F# Bm   G D/F# D   Em7 D/F#]
  Salvation song.

Verse 2:
Your sunrise on a darkened land;
Long shadows, by noon no where to stand.
The lost come; by Your blood they are redeemed,
Together we will sing:

Chorus 2:
       G   A
That we love You, O King Jesus,
  Bm   Bm/A   Gmaj7
Forever You're the Lover of my soul.
       G   A
As Your presence falls upon us,
  Bm   Bm/A
Your glory now revealed,
  Gmaj7   D/F#   Em9
And God, we pray Your song will fill our land.
  A7   Bm   F#m7   G   A7sus4   D2
Salvation song.

Taken from
BREATHE
Andy Smith
SURCD5073

YOU'RE MIGHTY AND STRONG TO SAVE

Johnny Parks, Nick Herbert
& Cathy Parks

Rescuer

C   F   Am   G   F6/9

Verse:
     C   F
You're mighty and strong to save,
     C   F
You're mighty and strong to save,
     C   F
You're mighty and strong to save,
       C   F
Rescuer.   [Repeat]

Bridge:
          C   F   C   F
From the heaven's You came, to the depths of the grave
     C   F   C   F
To redeem for Your praise: Rescuer.
       C   F   C   F
Jesus, You overcame death itself for our sake
       C   F   Am G
Let the world now proclaim: Rescuer.

Chorus:
          C
Oh, what a   Saviour!
         Am
Freedom for - ever,
       G   F
We lift our hands with chains undone.
                 C
Hearts that know   mercy
          Am
Cannot stay   silent,
       G   F
We sing our songs of saving love.

Fill: C F6/9 C F6/9

Ending:
      C
You're mighty and strong to save,
       Am
You're mighty and strong to save,
      G
You're mighty and strong to save,
      F
Rescuer.   [Repeat]
[Last time]:
      C   F6/9   C   F6/9   C
Rescuer.

Taken from
BREAK THE SILENCE
Johnny Parks Band
SURCD5095

YOU'RE SCARED YOU'LL LOSE THIS FIGHT 168.

Almost there

Tré & Tori Sheppard, Mark Prentice,
Paul Baker, Jonny Ravn & Steve Evans

A2/C♯ E/G♯ G♯m7 A2 E A/C♯ F♯m7 C♯m7 B/D♯

Verse 1:
A2/C♯   E/G♯   G♯m7
    You're scared you'll lose this fight,
A2/C♯   E/G♯   G♯m7   A2/C♯
    You're running out of time,
      E/G♯   G♯m7   A2
This mountain seems too high to climb.

Chorus 1:
E   G♯m7 A/C♯
    It's gonna be   alright,
F♯m7   E
      'Cause you're almost there.
                G♯m7 A/C♯   F♯m7
    It's gonna be   alright.

Verse 2:
When you're ready to let go
Is when you're closest to hope,
And hope will carry you, I know.

Mid section:
C♯m7 B/D♯ E
You're still   waiting (and you cry sometimes)
C♯m7 B/D♯ E
Hope is   fading ('cause you just can't find)
C♯m7 B/D♯ E   A
Love   finds   you somehow (somehow it finds you).

Chorus 2&3:
E   G♯m7 A/C♯
    It's gonna be   alright,
F♯m7   E
      'Cause you're almost there.
                G♯m7 A/C♯   F♯m7 E   B/D♯   A/C♯
    It's gonna be   alright.
E   B/D♯ A/C♯ A   E
   It's gonna be alright,   you're almost there.

Taken from
AS SURE AS THE STARS
Onehundredhours
SURCD5089

YOU'RE THE GOD OF THIS CITY

God of this city

Aaron Boyd, Richard Bleakley, Peter Comfort,
Peter Kernaghan, Andrew McCann & Ian Jordan

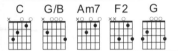

C   G/B   Am7   F2   G

Verse:

              C
You're the God of this city,
            G/B
You're the King of these people,
           Am7
You're the Lord of this nation,
     F2
You are.
             C
You're the light in this darkness,
           G/B
You're the hope to the hopeless,
           Am7
You're the peace to the restless,
     F2
You are.
C   G/B   F2
There is no one like our God.
Am7   G/B   F2
There is no one like our God.

Chorus 1-3:

    F2
For greater things have yet to come,
    G   C   G/B F2
And greater things are still to be done in this city.
F2
Greater things have yet to come,
    G   C   G/B F2
And greater things are still to be done in this city.

Chorus 4&5:

    F2
For greater things have yet to come,
    G   C   G/B F2
And greater things are still to be done in this city.
F2
Greater things have yet to come,
    G   C F2 C F Am7 F2 C2 F2 [Last time:] C
And greater things are still to be done here.

Taken from
GOD OF THIS CITY
Passion
SURCD5126

YOU'RE THE ONE

Andy Smith

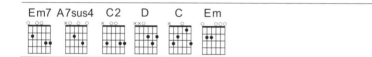

Em7 A7sus4 C2 D C Em

Capo 1

Verse 1:
Em7
  You're the One, the Holy King.
A7sus4
  I trust in You for ev'rything.
Em7
  I boast in You, You're all I need,
A7sus4   Em7
  And I believe we're gonna see
A7sus4   C2   D
  The goodness of the Lord. [1st time repeat]

Bridge:
Em7   A7sus4
  I want to belong
Em7   A7sus4
  To a generation that is strong.
Em7   A7sus4
  Laying hold of Your kingdom,
C
  We prophesy to the breath:
D
  Let the army arise.

Chorus:
Em7   A7sus4
  We will fight and we will run
Em7   A7sus4
  Headlong into the battle till it's won.
Em7   A7sus4
  Your name's renown is what we raise;
Em7   A7sus4   Em [C Em C Em C Em C]
  Jesus, come and take Your place.

Verse 2:
You call us now to higher things,
To live a life of love for You;
Unity is what we need,
So let the church arise
And see the glory of the Lord.

Verse 3:
Your promises are gonna be,
'Cause idle words You do not speak.
Streams of life flow unrestrained.
You're gonna move like we've never seen.
The lost will be redeemed.

Taken from
BREATHE
Andy Smith
SURCD5073

YOU'RE THE ONE

Verse 1:
Fm7
   You're the One, the Holy King.
B♭7sus4
   I trust in You for ev'rything.
Fm7
   I boast in You, You're all I need,
B♭7sus4   Fm7
   And I believe we're gonna see
B♭7sus4   D♭2   E♭
   The goodness of the Lord. [1st time repeat]

Bridge:
Fm7   B♭7sus4
   I want to belong
Fm7   B♭7sus4
   To a generation that is strong.
Fm7   B♭7sus4
   Laying hold of Your kingdom,
D♭
   We prophesy to the breath:
E♭
   Let the army arise.

Chorus:
Fm7   B♭7sus4
   We will fight and we will run
Fm7   B♭7sus4
   Headlong into the battle till it's won.
Fm7   B♭7sus4
   Your name's renown is what we raise;
Fm7   B♭7sus4   Fm [D♭   Fm   D♭   Fm   D♭   Fm   D♭]
   Jesus, come and take Your place.

Verse 2:
You call us now to higher things,
To live a life of love for You;
Unity is what we need,
So let the church arise
And see the glory of the Lord.

Verse 3:
Your promises are gonna be,
'Cause idle words You do not speak.
Streams of life flow unrestrained.
You're gonna move like we've never seen.
The lost will be redeemed.

Taken from
BREATHE
Andy Smith
SURCD5073

YOUR LOVE, O GOD

Beautiful Jesus

Kristian Stanfill

| A | E/G♯ | F♯m | D | D2 | F♯m7 | Esus4 | Bm7 |

Verse 1:
A
Your love, O God,
  E/G♯
Displayed for us
    F♯m   D
As crimson covered over sinless hands.
   A
Your majesty
  E/G♯
For all to see
  F♯m   D
In raging storms and quiet cloudless days.

Chorus:
          A
Beautiful Jesus,
        D2
Beautiful Saviour,
           F♯m7   Esus4
Nothing is greater, brilliant creator,
         D2
Friend of mine.
[Not 1st time:]
        A
Perfect in power,
        D2
Matchless in glory.
         F♯m7   Esus4
Nothing is greater, brilliant creator,
         D2
Friend of mine.

Mid section:
   A
My lips will sing,
   Bm7
My heart will bring
D2
Praise to You, the holy King.   [Repeat]

Last chorus:
Beautiful Jesus, beautiful Saviour,
Nothing is greater, brilliant creator,
Friend of mine.
Perfect in power, matchless in glory.
Nothing is greater, brilliant creator,
         A   Bm7
Nothing is greater, brilliant creator,
        F♯m7   Esus4
Nothing is greater, brilliant creator,
     E   D2
Friend of mine.

Verse 2:
You're powerful,
Above this world.
The universe is under Your command.
Your glory shines
A holy light
That leads our hearts to praise,
Your holy name is on our lips.

Copyright © 2008 worshiptogether.com songs/sixsteps Music/Adm by kingswaysongs.com
for the UK & Europe tym@kingsway.co.uk. Used by permission.

Taken from
GOD OF THIS CITY
Passion
SURCD5126

YOUR MERCY TAUGHT US

(Dancing generation)

Matt Redman

D   Bm   G   Em   D/F♯   A7sus4

Intro: D   Bm

Verse:

    D
Your mercy taught us how to dance,
  Bm
To celebrate with all we have,
      G   D
And we'll dance to thank You for mercy.

Your glory taught us how to shout,
    Bm
We'll lift Your name in all the earth,
    G   D
And we'll shout to the praise of Your glory.

Bridge:

      Em   D/F♯
It's the overflow of a forgiven soul,
         G
And now we've seen You, God,
    A7sus4
Our hearts cannot stay silent.

Chorus:

    D
And we'll be a dancing generation,
Em   G
Dancing because of Your great mercy, Lord,
           D
Your great mercy, Lord.

And we'll be a shouting generation,
Em   G
Shouting because of Your great glory, Lord,
          D
Your great glory, Lord.

Taken from
FACEDOWN
Matt Redman
SURCD5007
&
NEWDAY: YOU REIGN
Newday
SURCD5049

YOUR VOICE STILLS THE OCEAN

Nothing is impossible

Al Gordon, Hanif Wiliiams
& Tim Hughes

Em C G D/F♯ D Am D/A

Verse 1:
Em   C
  Your voice stills the ocean,
G   D/F♯
  One word heals the broken.
Em   C
  Your power is uncontainable,
G   D
Awesome God.
Em   C
  Such strength born in weakness,
G   D/F♯
  Your life lights the darkness.
Em   C
  You died and rose - a miracle,
G   D
Awesome God.

Bridge:
Am   Em   D
Jesus, we believe;
Am   Em   D
Saviour, we believe

Chorus:
      C
That nothing is impossible,
  G   D/F♯
Nothing is impossible,
  C
Nothing is impossible
      G   D
For You.
     C
You're the God of miracles,
 D   Em
Risen and invincible.
   C
Nothing is impossible
      G D C   G D/A [2.] Em D/F♯ G D/F♯ G D/A C
For You.

Verse 2:
You speak: mountains tremble,
One move: kings are humbled.
Your plans are undefeatable,
Awesome God.
We know if God is for us,
Who can be against us?
You make us more than conquerors,
Awesome God.

Taken from
FUTURE SOUND
Al Gordon
SURCD5125

YOUR WAYS ARE ALWAYS GREATER

174.

Never let me go

Ben Cantelon & Tim Hughes

E/G♯   A   D   Bm   F♯m

Verse 1:
E/G♯   A   D
   Your ways are always greater,
E/G♯   A   D
   Though I may not see.
E/G♯   A   D   E/G♯   A   D
   Your promise is written on my heart.

Verse 2:
I look to You, my Saviour,
When I am weak.
I find rest in the shadow of Your wing.

Chorus:
E/G♯   A   D
   Father,   I know You'll never let me go,
E/G♯   A   D
   You're always there;
E/G♯   A   D
   And when the darkness is surrounding
         E/G♯ A   D
Still You love me so,
         E/G♯ A D
Yes, You love me so.

Verse 3:
You word is never-failing,
Strength for today.
I have hidden Your word in my heart.

Mid section:
        Bm   A   F♯m
You are strength for today
              A   E
And bright hope for tomorrow.
        Bm   A   F♯m
You are strength for today
              A   E
And bright hope for tomorrow. [Repeat]

Taken from
DAYLIGHT BREAKS THROUGH
Ben Cantelon
SURCD5094

YOU STOOD BEFORE CREATION

(The stand)

Joel Houston

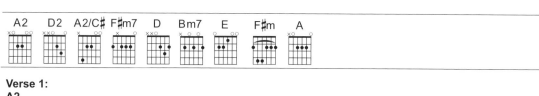

A2   D2   A2/C♯ F♯m7   D   Bm7   E   F♯m   A

Verse 1:
A2
You stood before creation,
  D2
Eternity in Your hand;
A2/C♯   F♯m7
You spoke the earth into motion,
          D   D2
My soul now to stand.

Verse 2:
You stood before my failure
And carried the cross for my shame;
My sin weighed upon Your shoulders,
My soul now to stand.

Chorus
D2
  So what can I say,
Bm7   F♯m7
  And what could I do,
            D2
But offer this heart, O God,
E   [F♯m last x D]
  Completely to You.

Verse 3:
I'll walk upon salvation,
Your Spirit alive in me;
This life to declare Your promise:
My soul now to stand.

Chorus
D2
  So what can I say,
Bm7   F♯m7 A2
  And what could I do,
          Bm7
But offer this heart, O God,
E   D   A [E F♯m7 D A (ad lib repeat)] E F♯m7
  Completely to You.

D   A   E   F♯m7   D
  So I'll stand with arms high and heart abandoned
  A   E   F♯m7   D
In awe of the One who gave it all.
   A   E   F♯m7
I'll stand, my soul, Lord, to You surrendered;
D   A   E F♯m E
All I am is Yours.
            D2
So what can I say . . .

Taken from
LOVE CAME DOWN
Soul Survivor Live 2006
SURCD5076

YOU TOLD ME, BUT I COULDN'T BELIEVE IT   176.

I can't see myself

Tré & Tori Sheppard
& Paul Baker

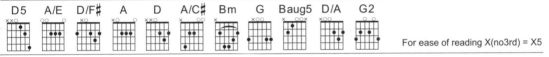

D5   A/E   D/F♯   A   D   A/C♯   Bm   G   Baug5   D/A   G2

For ease of reading X(no3rd) = X5

Capo 2

Verse 1:
E5(D5)   B/F♯(A/E)   E/G♯(D/F♯)   B(A)   E5(D5)
   You told me,
But I couldn't believe it.
                B/F♯(A/E)   E/G♯(D/F♯)   B(A)   E5(D5)
So You showed me
But I couldn't see it, 'cause

Chorus:
E(D)   B/D♯(A/C♯)   C♯m(Bm)   A(G)
I can't see   myself   the way You see me
     E(D)   B/D♯(A/C♯)   C♯m(Bm)
And I'm sick of   myself,
       A(G)   E5(D5)
Maybe You could heal me.

[2nd time:]
C♯m(Bm)
   From the whispers
Caug5(Baug5)
   And the questions,
E/B(D/A)   A2(G2)   E5(D5)
   You love me - why?

[Last time:]
E5(D5)
   Come heal me, come heal me.

Verse 2:
I'm blinded,
And buried beneath it all.
And I need You
To help me see what You saw.

Taken from
AS SURE AS THE STARS
Onehundredhours
SURCD5089

YOU TOOK UPON YOURSELF THE BLAME   177.

Worthy

Ben Cantelon

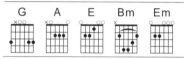

G   A   E   Bm   Em

Capo 3

Verse 1:
<pre>
              B♭(G)   C(A)
You took upon Yourself the blame,
              B♭(G)   C(A)
You took upon Yourself my shame,
              B♭(G)   C(A)   G(E)
You took upon Yourself so that I   may be free.
</pre>

Verse 2:
You came and gave Your life willingly;
The greatest sacrifice.
Fit for a King,
You came and gave Your life
So that I may be free.

Chorus:
<pre>
        B♭(G)   C(A)
You're worthy of honour,
        Dm(Bm) C(A)
You're worthy of praise.
B♭(G)   C(A)
First and the Last,
            Dm(Bm)   C(A)
You're my saving grace.
</pre>

Verse 3:
You deserve the highest praise;
All creation bows
At the sound of Your name.
All the angels sing:
'Glory to the King'.

Mid section:
<pre>
        B♭(G)   C(A)
And You have no beginning,
     Dm(Bm)   C(A)
You conquered the grave.
        B♭(G)   C(A)
The whole earth will resound
       G(E)
And together we will sing:
B♭(G) C(A)   Dm(Bm) C(A)
Glory,   hallelujah, glory.
B♭(G) C(A)   Dm(Bm) C(A)
Glory,   hallelujah, glory.
         Gm(Em)
And for all You've done,
Dm(Bm)   C(A)
  The price You've paid,
       B♭(G)   C(A)
We'll join in the song   of the redeemed.
</pre>

Taken from
DAYLIGHT BREAKS THROUGH
Ben Cantelon
SURCD5094

Tracing threads that run through the Bible

Andy Croft & Mike Pilavachi

Chapter 4: The Presence Thread

Have you ever been to a church meeting or service and, while you've been singing the same songs with the usual people in the same building, suddenly there is something that's indefinably different? It may be that as the last chords of a song fade away, nobody moves. You can't even hear the usual coughs; the atmosphere is electric; there's a heaviness that you can almost feel. . . nobody wants the worship to end. What is going on? Quite probably God has 'manifested' his presence – in other words, it's as if he's just shown up. But this begs the question: hasn't he been there all along? Isn't he everywhere? Or does he sometimes give church a miss?

Of course *God is everywhere*. . . always. The technical term for this is 'omnipresent'. He didn't just light the fuse and walk away when he created the universe – it's God who, through Christ, sustains the universe every moment of its being. Colossians 1:17 reads, 'He is before all things, and in him all things hold together.' Also God is *always* present when his people come together to worship him. Jesus said, 'Where two or three come together in my name, there am I with them' (Matthew 18:20). He never misses church whether he seems to be there or not. This is clearly the teaching of the Bible.

At the same time we see that there are particular times when God manifests his presence in order to bless, rebuke, empower, comfort or speak in a particular way. The burning bush; the dedication of the Temple; Isaiah's vision; the Day of Pentecost; the vision of John in Revelation, and supremely in the person of Jesus. . . these are just a few examples of the many times in the Bible that God appears in a particular way. So in the Bible we see God is everywhere, and at the same time he manifests himself at particular times and in particular places.

Thirdly, we also see the presence of God 'indwells', i.e. lives in the people of God. In the Old Testament God's Spirit filled prophets, priests and kings. From the Day of Pentecost in Acts 2 the same Spirit is poured out on 'all flesh'. It is no longer exclusively for prophets, priests and kings; rather, all who ask for it will receive.

There are three words we see all over the Bible: 'presence', 'glory' and 'holy'. In this chapter we want to define these words and show how they are inseparable. Still, we are getting ahead of ourselves; let's start tracing this golden thread from its genesis, the Garden of Eden. . .

God longs to be present with his people

As we have already seen, God created Adam and Eve for fellowship with him; they spent time walking round the Garden with God and talking to him face-to-face. After they disobeyed God and because of their sin, they were too ashamed to be in his presence and so hid in the Garden. Humanity ran away and hid from the presence of God. How many of us, when we sin, want to go and sit with God straight away? Once Adam and Eve had been made to leave Eden they realised what it was to be outside the presence of God. Looking around them they no longer saw paradise, they saw parched, barren, desolate land, and looking at each other they saw their bodies age. What was different between the Garden and the wasteland? Between the place of life and death? Was it simply that Eden had better soil? No, the difference was that it was in Eden that God chose to manifest his presence. This was where he hung out and, where the presence of God is, there is life! Paradise had been lost; sin and death came into the world.

Years later God manifested his presence in the desert of Midian to a fugitive called Moses. Walking the sheep one day, Moses came across a bush that was a little different from all the other bushes. God appeared to him at the burning bush, and when Moses approached, God said, 'Take off your sandals, for the place where you are standing is holy ground' (Exodus 3:5). In Eden, Adam and Eve could hang out with God and not worry about anything. After sin had come into the world this was no longer the case. Moses, before approaching the Lord, was made to remove his sandals. God's presence now had to be approached with caution; removing the sandals was an attempt to remove anything that might be impure before drawing near to God's holiness. It's like going to your posh relatives' home. You've just been playing footy, are covered in mud and on the way step in dog poo. You walk into their home, march over their beautiful white carpet and kiss your aunt on both cheeks – she looks horrified! You think 'What's wrong with my kiss?' Then you realise she's looking beyond you. You glance down and dog poo footprints are covering the carpet. At the burning bush, Moses' sin was like a dog poo on God's holy carpet. . .

Israel must make an effort

Having rescued Israel through Moses God moved into the Israelite camp. He gave them detailed plans to build a Tabernacle: 'Have them make a sanctuary for me, and I will dwell among them. Make this tabernacle and all its furnishings exactly like the pattern I will show you' (Exodus 25:8–9). The Tabernacle was a kind of tent, but it was more than a tent – the word in the Hebrew means 'the place of divine dwelling'. It was no small thing for the absolute holy God to choose to live among unholy people. He gave them an instruction manual much more complicated than any you'd find at Ikea. The point was not that he was fussy about his furniture, but that God would live among his people on his own terms. Strict instructions were aimed at protecting and honouring the holiness of God. The Tabernacle had 'zones' of increasing holiness: there was an outer court, a 'holy place' and a 'Most Holy Place'. It was in the Most Holy Place, the Holy of Holies, that the presence of God rested, and this was separated from the rest of the tent by a thick veil.

It's difficult for us in the twenty-first century to understand the rituals that were carried out before going into the tent where God lived (let alone the actual room in the tent where his presence rested); many of them seem very odd! It's a bit like some of the bizarre rituals we go through today before going on a first date. We wash very carefully, we may get the hair straighteners out, we'll select just the right perfume and exactly the right outfit; it's only having looked in the mirror for the sixteenth time that we're ready (and that's just the guys). As men, we know that often by the third date women are *telling us* what they want us to wear and smell like.

That's what it was *always* like for Israel's representatives (the priests) before any big date in the presence of God. Our girlfriends may say, 'Make sure you wear Hugo Boss (not the other rubbish) and wear your best shirt (the one without the stains).' The reason many of us do what we're told is partly because we're 'under the thumb', but mainly because by making an effort we can sit in her presence at dinner, or on the sofa, with that extra bit of confidence. God told the priests the smell he wanted them to have, the special clothes they were to wear and the equipment they were to use. There was unique oil that was to be used only on the priests, and unique incense that was to be burned only in the Holy of Holies, all the temple equipment had been made to an exact design and dedicated to the Lord. Out of total awe and reverence for the holy God, a huge effort was made when one was only near to his presence.

But that's not all. Only one person per year, the high priest, was actually allowed *into* the Holy of Holies, into the presence of God. The day on which the high priest entered the presence of God was called the Day of Atonement. To 'atone' is to make up for sin. The English word 'atonement' is derived from 'at-one-ment'. So to atone is to make up for sin but it's also to bring about a reunion, a oneness, between us and God! Atonement was symbolised by sacrifice; the high priest would sacrifice animals for his own sins and then for those of the people. This was the one time of the year that anyone was allowed behind the veil that separated off the Holy of Holies, the room where God dwelt. One of the meanings of the word holiness is 'to separate' or 'to cut off'. A holy day is separated from other days; holy ground is separated from other ground. What is it that makes something holy? The answer in the Old Testament seems to be the presence of God. Holy days were those given over to God and holy objects were those dedicated to God. *What made the Tabernacle holy was nothing other than God's presence*; it is no coincidence that the holiest place in the tent was the room where he lived!

God is holy and so has to be 'set apart' from sin. At the same time, this holy God longed to dwell among his people. By giving Israel the law, God sought to make for himself a holy people. By setting up the Tabernacle and placing strict regulations around it he sought to live among his holy people. He wasn't fussy but he was pure. The regulations are God saying to his people, 'There's nothing I want more than to live with you but you've got to make an effort because I am holy.' The Tabernacle was the place that the very presence of God himself – the holy and separate God – dwelt in the midst of his people. Another name for the Tabernacle was the 'Tent of Meeting' and it became, in effect, God's address on earth. Exodus 40:34–35 gives a description of God moving into his new address: 'Then the cloud covered the Tent of Meeting, and the glory of the LORD filled the tabernacle. Moses could not enter the Tent of Meeting because the cloud had settled upon it, and the glory of the LORD filled the tabernacle.'

So, God has been longing to be close to humanity. They had hidden from him when they sinned in Eden and his holiness meant he couldn't stand their sin. At last in Israel, a people whom he specially chose and to whom he's given instructions on how to be near him, God has found a way to rebuild this intimate relationship. He says to Israel that if they follow these instructions, 'I will walk among you and be your God' (Leviticus 26:12).

The presence is *everything*

A story in 1 Samuel chapters 4–6 tells us more about what it is to have and to lose the presence of God. The people of Israel were getting beaten up by the Philistines. So someone had a great idea to bring the ark of the covenant from the town called Shiloh where it was being kept. It was the ark that symbolised the presence of God and it was made to house the stone tablets on which were written the Ten Commandments. It also contained the staff of Aaron (Moses' brother), which had miraculously blossomed, and a jar of the manna God had sent to feed Israel in the wilderness. It was the centrepiece of the Holy of Holies and God dwelt above it. They figured that by bringing the actual physical dwelling of God onto the battlefield with them they couldn't lose. . .

The Philistines won the battle and captured the ark of God – the Israelites had made the mistake of using God's holy presence as a good luck charm. When the pregnant wife of Phinehas (one of the two priests who looked after the ark) was told that her husband had been killed and that the ark of the covenant was in the hands of the Philistines, she, in her distress, began to give birth prematurely. As she was dying she named her new-born son Ichabod (which means 'no glory'), saying, 'The glory has departed from Israel' (1 Samuel 4:21).

If the capture of the ark was a disaster for Israel it was a total nightmare for the Philistines! They made the mistake of parking God's presence next to the image of their own god, Dagon. In the morning the statue of Dagon was in pieces on the floor, face down before the ark of God. Then the Philistines started growing tumours and dying. They realised that they were being judged in the presence of the God of Israel and so they put the ark on a cart and hitched it to a cow. The cow of its own accord led the ark back into Israel.

From this story we learn the power of the presence of God. Sometimes we in the church can treat God's presence simply as a teddy bear; but he is an awesome, terrible and holy God. It can be wonderful for those who are the people of God and who choose to honour his holiness. It can be terrible for those who are not the people of God or who choose to lead lives of rebellion against God. The point of this story is that Mrs Phinehas and the rest of Israel *knew* when God's glory had departed. The question is in our rational, intellectual, sophisticated, twenty-first-century church, do we?

A famous evangelist used to pose the challenge, 'If the Holy Spirit left your church, would anybody notice?' That is one of the big questions we, the church, have to answer in our day. The longing in people's hearts ought not to be for a church that is more slick, entertaining or comfortable; the desperate need is for a church that is more filled with the presence of God.

Later in the story of the Bible we see that King David planned, and his son King Solomon built, a permanent temple for God. Until this point, God's address had been the Tabernacle constructed by Moses. The Temple was built in the centre of Jerusalem and, just like the Tabernacle, was designed with zones of holiness. The Holy of Holies was the focus of the Temple. The heart of Israel's worship was Jerusalem. It was in Jerusalem that the whole population was to gather for major festivals; the heart of Jerusalem was the Temple, the heart of the Temple was the Holy of Holies and the heart-beat of the Holy of Holies was *the manifest presence of God*.

Another key story that helps us understand the significance and importance of the presence of God can be found in 2 Chronicles chapters 5–7. It tells us of the completion and dedication of the

Temple. The ark is brought into the Most Holy Place; the priests, the trumpeters and the singers all praise God, singing:

> 'He is good; his love endures for ever.' Then the temple of the LORD was filled with a cloud, and the priests could not perform their service because of the cloud, for the glory of the LORD filled the temple of God. (2 Chronicles 5:13)

At this point Solomon gets up and prays a long prayer of dedication, at the end of which we read:

> When Solomon finished praying, fire came down from heaven and consumed the burnt offering and the sacrifices, and the glory of the LORD filled the temple. The priests could not enter the temple of the LORD because the glory of the LORD filled it. When all the Israelites saw the fire coming down and the glory of the LORD above the temple, they knelt on the pavement with their faces to the ground, and they worshipped and gave thanks to the LORD, saying, 'He is good; his love endures for ever.' (2 Chronicles 7:1–3)

What an amazing meeting! Have you ever wondered what *is* the glory of God? The glory of God here is shown to be the manifest presence of God. If there's one thing it makes explicit it's that you KNOW when the glory of God arrives. Just as Phinehas' wife knew when the glory had departed from Israel, so the Israelites knew when the glory fell on the Temple; it wasn't just an intellectual realisation, it was unquestionably an experience.

Our friend Matt Redman wrote a song, the first verse of which says, 'Lord let your glory fall as on that ancient day, songs of enduring love and then your glory came. And as a sign to you that we would love the same, our hearts will sing this song, Lord let your glory come!' He was talking about *that* ancient day, the day the glory of God fell on his Temple. In this modern day, we need to do more than just sing another Matt Redman song; we need to cry, to call out to God, for his glory to fall. We will only really do that when we truly realise that it is the presence of God which makes all the difference.

These stories show us that to live in God's presence is what we were created for – remember Eden – and that God is doing everything to live among his people. Moses understood the necessity of living in the presence of God. In Exodus 33 he told God, 'If your Presence does not go with us [Israel], do not send us up from here. . . What else will distinguish me and your people from all the other people on the face of the earth?' (Exodus 33:14–16). Moses had learnt the lesson that to go even into the Promised Land (a land of plenty and prosperity) without the presence of God is a waste of time. It was God's presence that marked Israel out as God's people. Christians today are not, generally, better looking, funnier, better dressed or smarter than non-Christians. God's presence and God's presence alone distinguishes us. It was only God's presence that gave meaning to the Tabernacle and then to the Temple as the place of worship. It is all about his presence!

The presence is lost

The prophetic book of Ezekiel is one of the wackiest in the Bible. We meet wheels within wheels, chariots of fire and a man who passes 390 days lying on one side, in addition to shaving all his hair off in order to perform different crazy but symbolic acts with it. . . we can understand why Ezekiel might be thought to be one sandwich short of the full picnic. However, the book of Ezekiel is a key to a deeper understanding of the meaning of the glorious presence of our God.

Ezekiel received his visions while with the Israelites in exile in Babylon. In chapter 10 Ezekiel has a vision in which he's transported to the Temple back in Jerusalem. In the Temple he is shown four horrendous scenes. They are different scenes of the people of Israel worshipping idols and they highlight how Israel is sinning on the very doorstep of God's house. The last and worst act Ezekiel is shown is in the inner court of the Temple, just outside the sanctuary of God. Here there are 25 men, with their backs to the sanctuary, prostrating themselves and worshipping the sun. The seriousness, scale and shame of this sin is huge. Imagine returning home to find not only that your wife or husband is committing adultery, but that, disgustingly, they've been having sex in the bed the two of you are meant to share. . . Israel's repeated sin penetrated even to the most sacred of places. The holy God had longed to dwell with his people. Since their time in Egypt, Israel had been repeatedly turning away from God. He had sent them warning after warning, prophet after prophet, trying and trying to call his rebellious people back to him.

The holy God, the God who kept himself separate from all that was unholy, had set aside the Temple as his dwelling place. It is no coincidence that when describing Israel's sin Ezekiel repeatedly uses the phrase 'to profane' – the opposite of 'to make holy' (the word 'profane' in Ezekiel makes up 39 of its 71 appearances in the Bible).

It is often the holy name of God that is described as being profaned, and in one striking phrase God himself announces, 'You have profaned me' (Ezekiel 13:19). Ezekiel's vision tells us that even the corner among his people that God had claimed as holy ground was being used to worship other gods. In effect his home, the place on earth where he had chosen to dwell, had, in a spiritual sense, been broken into, spat on, defiled, trampled over and scorned.

The holy God could no longer dwell in such a place and so, reluctantly but without a choice, he packed his bags and he left his home among his people. In Ezekiel's vision he sees the glory of the Lord depart from the Temple. The glory hovers at the edge of the Temple; it's as if God is having one last look around before he finally leaves (Ezekiel 10). It is because the holiness of God is offended that the glory of God leaves. God's address was no longer in Jerusalem and this proved to have disastrous consequences. The people of Israel, just before Jerusalem was destroyed, thought their city was indestructible. How could anyone come close to conquering Jerusalem – it was where God lived! In 586 BC the king of Babylon crushed the city and destroyed the Temple. This would have sent shockwaves throughout Israel – the place where God lived had been conquered! Ezekiel would have agreed that the place God chose to live in was indestructible. The point was he no longer lived in Jerusalem! The presence of God had left the Temple.

The presence will return. . . eventually

Having predicted the fall of Jerusalem, Ezekiel went on to prophesy about the day Israel would return from exile. In Ezekiel 40–48 he has a vision of a new Temple being built and the glory of the Lord returning to dwell among his people. This vision carries echoes of the paradise of Eden; a river is seen flowing from the south side of the altar in the Temple. In the Bible water is symbolic of life and particularly the Holy Spirit. It's when the presence of the living God returns to the Temple that life returns to Israel.

As the river flows out from the Temple in the vision, the dry, parched, barren, dead land becomes rich, abundant, and overflows with goodness. Ezekiel tells us that 'where the river flows everything will live' (Ezekiel 47:9). Furthermore he prophesies that this sanctuary is to surpass the old one; the Lord intends to 'put my sanctuary among them for ever. My dwelling-place will be with them; I will be their God, and they will be my people. Then the nations will know that I the LORD make Israel holy, when my sanctuary is among them for ever' (Ezekiel 37:26–28).

Eventually the people of Israel started to return from exile. One of the first things they did was begin to rebuild the Temple at Jerusalem. This is recorded in the book of Ezra and Nehemiah. Ezra tells us that those who remembered the old Temple wept when they saw the new one being built:

> All the people gave a great shout of praise to the LORD, because the foundation of the house of the LORD was laid. But many of the older priests and Levites and family heads, who had seen the former temple, wept aloud when they saw the foundation of this temple being laid, while many others shouted for joy. (Ezra 3:11–12)

Why did they weep? Nobody knows for sure. It could have been that the new Temple was much smaller and plainer than the old Temple; it could have been that they just didn't like the colour scheme. It could have been, however, that the older priests who remembered the first Temple realised that something was missing, or rather Someone: this time there is no account of God manifesting his presence.

In our travels we have visited some churches that have made our mouths water because of all the stuff they have: sound systems that would be an engineer's dream; lighting that wouldn't look out of place at Wembley; soft, comfortable chairs; coffee shops and slick presentations. And yet, to be honest, sometimes we've been bored. Then we've sometimes been to other churches where, as we've walked through the door, we've thought, 'This place could do with a coat of paint and a bit of air freshener.' Yet as the meeting has started it's impossible not to recognise it: the manifest presence of God. When God shows up people don't care how hard the seats are! This is not to say we haven't encountered the manifest presence of God in some very nice buildings. . . the point is that the presence of God, not the building, matters. The dedication of this new Temple in Ezra 6 is different. The glory fell at the dedication of the Tabernacle in the wilderness; it fell at the dedication of the first Temple under Solomon; yet it is notably absent in the dedication of the second Temple. But what of Ezekiel's visions? Didn't he predict that the glory would return? Didn't he tell us that a river of life would flow? Perhaps the older priests were thinking he had got it wrong. . . Enter Jesus.

To read the rest of this chapter, you can buy Storylines from www.survivor.co.uk, www.soulsurvivor.com or your local Christian bookshop.

Crazy love

Overwhelmed by a Relentless God
Francis Chan with Danae Yankoski

Chapter 1: Stop Praying

What if I said, "Stop praying"? What if I told you to stop talking *at* God for a while, but instead to take a long, hard look at Him before you speak another word? Solomon warned us not to rush into God's presence with words. That's what fools do. And often, that's what we do.

We are a culture that relies on technology over community, a society in which spoken and written words are cheap, easy to come by, and excessive. Our culture says anything goes; fear of God is almost unheard of. We are slow to listen, quick to speak, and quick to become angry.

The wise man comes to God without saying a word and stands in awe of Him. It may seem a hopeless endeavour, to gaze at the invisible God. But Romans 1:20 tells us that through creation, we see His "invisible qualities" and "divine nature."

Let's begin this book by gazing at God in silence. What I want you to do right now is to go online and look at the "Awe Factor" video at www.crazylovebook.com to get a taste of the awe factor of our God. Seriously—go do it.

Speechless? Amazed? Humbled?

When I first saw those images, I *had* to worship. I didn't want to speak to or share it with anyone. I just wanted to sit quietly and admire the Creator.

It's wild to think that most of these galaxies have been discovered only in the past few years, thanks to the Hubble telescope. They've been in the universe for thousands of years without humans even knowing about them.

Why would God create more than 350,000,000,000 galaxies (and this is a conservative estimate) that generations of people never saw or even knew existed? Do you think maybe it was to make us say, "Wow, God is unfathomably big"? Or perhaps God wanted us to see these pictures so that our response would be, "Who do I think I am?"

R. C. Sproul writes, "Men are never duly touched and impressed with a conviction of their insignificance, until they have contrasted themselves with the majesty of God."

Switch gears with me for a minute and think about the detailed intricacy of the other side of creation.

Did you know that a caterpillar has 228 separate and distinct muscles in its head? That's quite a few, for a bug. The average elm tree has approximately *6 million* leaves on it. And your own heart generates enough pressure as it pumps blood throughout your body that it could squirt blood up to 30 feet. (I've never tried this, and I don't recommend it.)

Have you ever thought about how diverse and creative God is? He didn't have to make hundreds of different kinds of bananas, but He did. He didn't have to put 3,000 different species of trees within one square mile in the Amazon jungle, but He did. God didn't have to create so many kinds of laughter. Think about the different sounds of your friends' laughs—wheezes, snorts, silent, loud, obnoxious.

How about the way plants defy gravity by drawing water upward from the ground into their stems and veins? Or did you know that spiders produce three kinds of silk? When they build their webs, they create sixty feet of silk in one hour, simultaneously producing special oil on their feet that prevents them from sticking to their own web. (Most of us hate spiders, but sixty feet an hour deserves some respect!) Coral plants are so sensitive that they can die if the water temperature varies by even one or two degrees.

Did you know that when you get goose bumps, the hair in your follicles is actually helping you stay warmer by trapping body heat? Or what about the simple fact that plants take in carbon dioxide (which is harmful to us) and produce oxygen (which we need to survive)? I'm sure you knew that, but have you ever marvelled at it? And these same poison-swallowing, life-giving plants came from tiny seeds that were placed in the dirt. Some were watered, some weren't; but after a few days they poked through the soil and out into the warm sunlight.

Whatever God's reasons for such diversity, creativity, and sophistication in the universe, on earth, and in our own bodies, the point of it all is His glory. God's art speaks of Himself, reflecting who He is and what He is like.

> The heavens declare the glory of God; the skies proclaim the work of his hands. Day after day they pour forth speech; night after night they display knowledge. There is no speech or language where their voice is not heard. Their voice goes out into all the earth, their words to the ends of the world.
> Psalm 19:1–4

This is why we are called to worship Him. His art, His handiwork, and His creation all echo the truth that He is glorious. There is no other like Him. He is the King of Kings, the Beginning and the End, the One who was and is and is to come. I know you've heard this before, but I don't want you to miss it.

I sometimes struggle with how to properly respond to God's magnitude in a world bent on ignoring or merely tolerating Him. But know this: God will not be tolerated. He instructs us to worship and fear Him.

Go back and reread the last two paragraphs. Go to the Web site www.crazylovebook.com and watch the "Just Stop and Think" fifteen minute video. Close this book if you need to, and meditate on the almighty One who dwells in unapproachable light, the glorious One.

There is an epidemic of spiritual amnesia going around, and none of us is immune. No matter how many fascinating details we learn about God's creation, no matter how many pictures we see of His galaxies, and no matter how many sunsets we watch, we still forget.

Most of us know that we are supposed to love and fear God; that we are supposed to read our Bibles and pray so that we can get to know Him better; that we are supposed to worship Him with our lives. But actually living it out is challenging.

It confuses us when loving God is hard. Shouldn't it be easy to love a God so wonderful? When we love God because we feel we *should* love Him, instead of genuinely loving out of our true selves, we have forgotten who God really is. Our amnesia is flaring up again.

It may sound "un-Christian" to say that on some mornings I don't feel like loving God, or I just forget to. But I do. In our world, where hundreds of things distract us from God, we have to intentionally and consistently remind ourselves of Him.

I recently attended my high school reunion. People kept coming up to me and saying, "She's *your* wife?" They were amazed, I guess, that a woman so beautiful would marry someone like me. It happened enough times that I took a good look at a photograph of the two of us. I, too, was taken aback. It *is* astonishing that my wife chooses to be with me - and not just because she is beautiful. I was reminded of the fullness of what I have been given in my wife.

We need the same sort of reminders about God's goodness. We are programmed to focus on what we don't have, bombarded multiple times throughout the day with what we need to buy that will make us feel happier or sexier or more at peace. This dissatisfaction transfers over to our thinking about God. We forget that we already have everything we need in Him. Because we don't often think about the reality of who God is, we quickly forget that He is worthy to be worshipped and loved. We are to fear Him. A.W. Tozer writes,

What comes into our minds when we think about God is the most important thing about us.... Worship is pure or base as the worshiper entertains high or low thoughts of God. For this reason the gravest question before the Church is always God Himself, and the most portentous fact about any man is not what he at a given time may say or do, but what he in his deep heart conceives God to be like.

If the "gravest question" before us really is what God Himself is like, how do we learn to know Him?

We have seen how He is the Creator of both the magnitude of the galaxies and the complexity of caterpillars. But what is He like? What are His characteristics? What are His defining attributes? How are we to fear Him? To speak to Him? Don't check out here. We need to be reminded of this stuff. It is both basic and crucial.

God is holy. A lot of people say that whatever you believe about God is fine, so long as you are sincere. But that is comparable to describing your friend in one instance as a three-hundred-pound sumo wrestler and in another as a five-foot-two, ninety-pound gymnast. No matter how sincere you are in your explanations, both descriptions of your friend simply cannot be true.

The preposterous part about our doing this to God is that He already has a name, an identity. We don't get to decide who God is. "God said to Moses, 'I am who I am" (Ex. 3:14).We don't change that.

To say that God is holy is to say that He is set apart, distinct from us. And because of His set apart–ness, there is no way we can ever fathom all of who He is. To the Jews, saying something three times demonstrated its perfection, so to call God "Holy, Holy, Holy" is to say that He is perfectly set apart, with nothing and no one to compare Him to. *That* is what it means to be "holy."

Many Spirit-filled authors have exhausted the thesaurus in order to describe God with the glory He deserves. His perfect holiness, by definition, assures us that our words can't contain Him. Isn't it a comfort to worship a God we cannot exaggerate?

God is eternal. Most of us would probably agree with that statement. But have you ever seriously meditated on what it means? Each of us had a beginning; everything in existence began on a particular day, at a specific time.

Everything, that is, but God. He always has been, since before there was an earth, a universe, or even angels. God exists outside of time, and since we are within time, there is no way we will ever totally grasp that concept.

Not being able to fully understand God is frustrating, but it is ridiculous for us to think we have the right to limit God to something we are capable of comprehending. What a stunted, insignificant god *that* would be! If my mind is the size of a soda can and God is the size of all the oceans, it would be stupid for me to say He is only the small amount of water I can scoop into my little can. God is so much bigger, so far beyond our time-encased, air/food/sleep–dependent lives.

Please stop here, even if just for a moment, and glorify the eternal God: "But you, O Lord, sit enthroned forever; your renown endures through all generations.... But you remain the same, and your years will never end" (Ps. 102:12, 27)

God is all-knowing. Isn't this an intimidating thought? Each of us, to some degree, fools our friends and family about who we really are. But it's impossible to do that with God. He knows each of us, deeply and specifically. He knows our thoughts before we think them, our actions before we commit them, whether we are lying down or sitting or walking around. He knows who we are and what we are about. We cannot escape Him, not even if we want to. When I grow weary of trying to be faithful to Him and want a break, it doesn't come as a surprise to God.

For David, God's knowledge led him to worship. He viewed it as wonderful and meaningful. He wrote in Psalm 139 that even in the darkness he couldn't hide from God; that while he was in his mother's womb, God was there.

Hebrews 4:13 says, "Nothing in all creation is hidden from God's sight. Everything is uncovered and laid bare before the eyes of him to whom we must give account." It is sobering to realize that this is the same God who is holy and eternal, the Maker of the billions of galaxies and thousands of tree species in the rainforest. This is the God who takes the time to know all the little details about each of us. He does not have to know us so well, but He chooses to.

God is all-powerful. Colossians 1:16 tells us that everything was created *for* God: "For by him all things were created: things in heaven and on earth, visible and invisible, whether thrones or powers or rulers or authorities; all things were created by him and for him."

Don't we live instead as though God is created for *us*, to do *our* bidding, to bless *us*, and to take care of *our* loved ones?

Psalm 115:3 reveals, "Our God is in heaven; he does whatever pleases him." Yet we keep on questioning Him: "Why did You make me with this body, instead of that one?" "Why are so many people dying of starvation?" "Why are there so many planets with nothing living on them?" "Why is my family so messed up?" "Why don't You make Yourself more obvious to the people who need You?

The answer to each of these questions is simply this: because He's God. He has more of a right to ask us why so many people are starving. As much as we want God to explain himself to us, His creation, we are in no place to demand that He give an account to us.

> All the peoples of the earth are regarded as nothing. He does as he pleases with the powers of heaven and the peoples of the earth. No one can hold back his hand or say to him: "What have you done?"
> Daniel 4:35

Can you worship a God who isn't obligated to explain His actions to you? Could it be your arrogance that makes you think God owes you an explanation?

Do you really believe that compared to God, "all the peoples of the earth are regarded as nothing," including you?

God is fair and just. One definition of justice is "reward and/or penalty as deserved." If what we truly deserved were up to us, we would end up with as many different answers as people who responded. But it isn't up to us, mostly because none of us are good.

God is the only Being who is good, and the standards are set by Him. Because God hates sin, He has to punish those guilty of sin. Maybe that's not an appealing standard. But to put it bluntly, when you get your own universe, you can make your own standards. When we disagree, let's not assume it's His reasoning that needs correction.

It takes a lot for us to comprehend God's total hatred for sin. We make excuses like, "Yes, I am prideful at times, but everyone struggles with pride." However, God says in Proverbs 8:13, "I *hate* pride and arrogance." You and I are not allowed to tell Him how much He can hate it. He can hate and punish it as severely as His justice demands.

God never excuses sin. And He is always consistent with that ethic. Whenever we start to question whether God really hates sin, we have only to think of the cross, where His Son was tortured, mocked, and beaten because of sin. *Our* sin.

No question about it: God hates and must punish sin. And He is totally just and fair in doing so.

Before the Throne

So far we have talked about things we can see with our own eyes, things we know about creation, and some of the attributes of God as revealed in the Bible. But many facets of God expand beyond our comprehension. He cannot be contained in this world, explained by our vocabulary, or grasped by our understanding.

Yet in Revelation 4 and Isaiah 6 we get two distinct glimpses of the heavenly throne room. Let me paint a bit of a word picture for you.

In Revelation, when John recounts his experience of seeing God, it's as though he's scrambling for earthly words to describe the vision he was privileged to see. He describes the One seated on the throne with two gems, "jasper and carnelian," and the area around the throne as a rainbow that looked like an emerald. God, the One on the throne, resembles radiant jewels more than flesh and blood.

This sort of poetic, artistic imagery can be difficult for those of us who don't think that way. So imagine the most stunning sunset you've ever seen. Remember the radiant colours splashed across the sky? The way you stopped to gaze at it in awe? And how the words *wow* and *beautiful* seemed so lacking? That's a small bit of what John is talking about in Revelation 4 as he attempts to articulate his vision of heaven's throne room.

John describes "flashes of lightning" and "rumblings and peals of thunder" coming from God's throne, a throne that must be unlike any other. He writes that before the throne are seven blazing torches and something like a sea of glass that looks like crystal. Using ordinary words, he does his best to describe a heavenly place and a holy God.

Most intriguing to me is how John describes those who surround the throne. First, there are the twenty-four elders dressed in white and wearing golden crowns. Next, John describes four six-winged beings with eyes all over their bodies and wings. One has the face of a lion, one of an ox, one of a man, and one of an eagle.

I try to imagine what it would be like if I actually saw one of these creatures out in the woods or down at the beach. I would probably pass out! It would be terrifying to see a being with the face of a lion and eyes "all around and within."

As if John's description isn't wild and strange enough, he then tells us what the beings are saying. The twenty-four elders cast their gold crowns before the One on the throne, fall on their faces before Him, and say, "You are worthy, our Lord and God, to receive glory and honour and power, for you created all things, and by your will they were created and have their being." At the same time, the four creatures never stop (day or night) saying, "Holy, holy, holy is the Lord God Almighty, who was, and is, and is to come!" Just imagine being in that room, surrounded by the elders chanting God's worth, and the creatures declaring God's holiness.

The prophet Isaiah also had a vision of God in His throne room, but this time it is a more direct picture: "I saw the Lord seated on a throne."

Wow. Isaiah saw that and lived? The Israelites hid themselves whenever God passed by their camp because they were too afraid to look at Him, even the back of Him as He moved away. They were scared they would die if they saw God.

But Isaiah looked and saw God. He writes that the bottom of God's robe filled the whole temple, and that the seraphim appeared above Him. The seraphim each had six wings, similar to the creatures John describes in Revelation. Isaiah says they called out to one another, saying, "Holy, holy, holy is the Lord Almighty; the whole earth is full of his glory!" Then the foundations shook and smoke filled the house, which is similar to John's description of flashes of lightning and peals of thunder.

Isaiah's description is less detailed than John's, but Isaiah shares more of his response to being in the throne room of God. His words reverberate in the wake of the smoky room and shaky foundation: "Woe is me.... I am ruined! For I am a man of unclean lips, and my eyes have seen the King, the Lord Almighty." And then one of the seraphim brings Isaiah a piece of burning coal that had been smouldering on the altar. The creature touches Isaiah's mouth with the hot coal and tells him that his guilt is taken away.

Both of these descriptions serve a purpose. John's helps us imagine what the throne room of God looks like, while Isaiah's reminds us what our only response to such a God should be.

May Isaiah's cry become our own. Woe is me ... we are a people of unclean lips!

Perhaps you need to take a deep breath after thinking about the God who made galaxies and caterpillars, the One who sits enthroned and eternally praised by beings so fascinating that were they photographed, it would make primetime news for weeks. If you are not staggered, go to Isaiah 6 and Revelation 4 and read the accounts aloud and slowly, doing your best to imagine what the authors describe.

The appropriate way to end this chapter is the same way we began it - by standing in awed silence before a mighty, fearsome God, whose tremendous worth becomes even more apparent as we see our own puny selves in comparison.

Index of titles and first lines

Authors' titles, where different from first lines are shown in *italics*